THE
THINKING
MACHINE

By JACQUES FUTRELLE

Illustrated by Charles Beck

**Stories selected and edited by Tony Simon,
Editorial Director, Elementary Division,
Scholastic Magazines**

SCHOLASTIC BOOK SERVICES
NEW YORK • TORONTO • LONDON • AUCKLAND • SYDNEY • TOKYO

ISBN: 0-590-08107-1

Copyright © 1959 by TAB Books, Inc. This edition is pub-
lished by Scholastic Book Services, a division of Scholastic
Magazines, Inc., by arrangement with May Futrelle, member
of the Authors League of America.

23 22 21 20 19 18 17 16 15 14 13 12 11   9/7 0 1 2 3/8
Printed in U.S.A.   11

CONTENTS

FOREWORD

Dear Mystery Fans:

Meet The Thinking Machine!

The Thinking Machine was one of America's first story-book scientist-detectives. He was a master at using his wits to solve problems that no one else could solve.

"The human mind can do anything," he would insist. "Nothing is impossible. Two and two always make four." The Thinking Machine would put his brain to work and in no time at all he would clear up another baffling mystery.

Jacques Futrelle, the author of the Thinking Machine stories, was an interesting man. Born in Pike County, Georgia, on April 9, 1875, he was in turn a theater manager, a newspaperman, and a magazine writer. His Thinking Machine stories helped other authors of detective stories to write better mysteries.

In 1912, Mr. Futrelle sailed from Europe on the *Titanic*. The liner hit an iceberg in the Atlantic Ocean, and the ship sank, causing the deaths of many people, including Mr. Futrelle. Lost with him were several Thinking Machine stories that had not yet been printed.

Though the Thinking Machine stories were written 50 years ago, they are still very exciting. Why? Because for the life of us, we can't solve the mystery in each one. Only one man can do that. He, of course, is Professor S. F. X. Van Dusen—The Thinking Machine!

Tony Simon—Editor

The Problem

of

Cell 13

THE world had heard of Professor Van Dusen as The Thinking Machine. It was a newspaper phrase applied to him at the time of a remarkable exhibition at chess; he had demonstrated then that a stranger to the game might, by sheer logic, defeat a champion who had devoted a lifetime to chess.

The Thinking Machine! He spent week after week, month after month, in his small laboratory. Only occasionally did Professor Van Dusen have visitors. And these were usually men who dropped in to discuss some scientific problem. One evening two of these men, Dr. Charles Ransome and Alfred Fielding, called to discuss a favorite theory.

"Such a thing is impossible," declared Dr. Ransome emphatically, in the course of the conversation.

"Nothing is impossible," declared The Thinking Machine. "The mind is master of all things. When science fully recognizes that fact a great advance will have been made."

Dr. Ransome laughed tolerantly.

"I've heard you say such things before," he said. "But they mean nothing. Mind may be master of matter, but it hasn't yet found a way to apply itself. There are some things that can't be *thought* out of existence, or rather which would not yield to any amount of thinking."

"What, for instance?" demanded the Professor.

Dr. Ransome was thoughtful for a moment as he smoked. "Well, say prison walls," he replied. "No man can *think* himself out of a cell. If he could, there would be no prisoners."

"A man can so use his brain that he can leave a cell, which is the same thing," snapped The Thinking Machine.

Dr. Ransome was slightly amused.

"Let's take a case," he said, after a moment. "Take a cell where prisoners under sentence of death are confined—men who are desperate and, would take any chance to escape. Suppose you were locked in such a cell. Could you escape?"

2

"Certainly," declared The Thinking Machine.

"Of course," said Mr. Fielding, who entered the conversation for the first time, "you might wreck the cell with an explosive—but inside, as a prisoner, you would have no access to anything like that."

"There would be nothing of that kind," said The Thinking Machine. "You might treat me precisely as you treated prisoners under sentence of death. Still I would leave the cell."

"Not unless you entered it with tools prepared to get out," said Dr. Ransome.

The Thinking Machine was visibly annoyed.

"Lock me in any cell in any prison anywhere at any time, wearing only what is necessary, and I'll escape in a week," he declared sharply.

Dr. Ransome sat up straight in the chair, interested. Mr. Fielding smiled.

"You mean you could actually *think* yourself out?" asked Dr. Ransome.

"I would get out," replied The Thinking Machine.

"Are you serious?"

"Certainly I am serious."

Dr. Ransome and Mr. Fielding were silent for a long time.

"Would you be willing to try it?" asked Mr. Fielding, finally.

Of course it was an absurd thing, but The Thinking Machine repeated his willingness to undertake the escape. So then and there it was decided upon.

3

"To begin immediately," added Dr. Ransome.

"I'd prefer that it begin tomorrow," said The Thinking Machine, "because . . ."

"No, now," said Mr. Fielding, flatly. "You are arrested and without any warning you are locked in a cell. You have no chance to communicate with friends. You are left there exactly under the same conditions that would be given to a man under sentence of death. Are you willing to try immediately?"

"Very well, then. Now," said The Thinking Machine, and he arose.

"Say, the death-cell in Chisholm Prison?"

"The death-cell in Chisholm Prison."

"And what will you wear?"

"As little as possible," said The Thinking Machine. "Shoes, stockings, trousers and a shirt."

"You will permit yourself to be searched, of course?"

"I am to be treated precisely as all prisoners are treated," said The Thinking Machine. "No more attention, and no less."

There were some details to be arranged in the matter of obtaining permission for the test. Everything was done satisfactorily by telephone. But the prison officials, to whom the experiment was explained on purely scientific grounds, were greatly bewildered. Professor Van Dusen would be the most distinguished prisoner they had ever had in their charge.

The Thinking Machine donned those things which he was to wear during his imprisonment. Then he called the little old woman who was his housekeeper, cook and maidservant.

"Martha," he said, "it is now twenty-seven minutes past nine o'clock. I am going away. One week from tonight, at half-past nine, these gentlemen and one, possibly two, others will take supper with me here. Remember Dr. Ransome is very fond of artichokes."

The three men were driven to Chisholm Prison, where the warden was awaiting them. He understood merely that the eminent Professor Van Dusen was to be his prisoner, if he could keep him, for one week; that he had committed no crime, but that he was to be treated as all other prisoners were treated.

"Search him," instructed Dr. Ransome.

The Thinking Machine was searched. Nothing was found on him; the pockets of the trousers were empty; the white, stiff-bosomed shirt he wore had no pocket. The shoes and stockings were removed, examined, then replaced.

"Are you sure you want to do this?" asked Dr. Ransome.

"Would you be convinced if I did not?" inquired The Thinking Machine in turn.

"No."

"Very well, then. I'll do it."

Dr. Ransome asked the warden: "It will be impossible for him to communicate with any one outside?"

"Absolutely impossible," replied the warden. "He will not be permitted writing materials of any sort."

"And your jailers, would they deliver a message from him?"

"Not one word, directly or indirectly," said the warden. "You may rest assured of that. They will report anything he might say, or turn over to me anything he might give them."

"That seems entirely satisfactory," said Mr. Fielding, who was becoming more and more interested in the problem.

"Of course, in the event he fails," said Dr. Ransome, "and asks for his liberty, you understand you are to set him free?"

"I understand," replied the warden.

The Thinking Machine stood listening. He said nothing until this was all ended, then: "I should like to make three small requests. You may grant them or not, as you wish."

"No special favors, now," warned Mr. Fielding.

"I am asking none," was the stiff response. "I would like to have some tooth powder—buy it yourself to see that it is tooth powder—and I should like to have one five-dollar and two ten-dollar bills."

Dr. Ransome, Mr. Fielding and the warden exchanged glances. They were not surprised at the request for tooth powder, but the request for money startled them.

"Is there any man with whom our friend would come in contact that he could bribe with twenty-five dollars?" Dr. Ransome asked the warden.

"Not for twenty-five hundred dollars," was the positive reply.

"Well, let him have the money," said Mr. Fielding. "I think it is harmless enough."

"And what is the third request?" asked Dr. Ransome.

"I should like to have my shoes polished."

Again the astonished glances were exchanged. This last request seemed the height of absurdity. They agreed to it at once. The Thinking Machine was led back into the prison from which he had undertaken to escape.

"Here is Cell 13," said the warden, stopping three doors down the steel corridor. "This is where we keep condemned prisoners. No one can leave it without my permission; and no one in it can communicate with the outside. I'll stake my reputation on that. It's only three doors back of my office and I can readily hear any unusual noise."

"Will this cell do, gentlemen?" asked The Thinking Machine.

"Admirably," was the reply.

The heavy steel door was thrown open. There was a great scurrying and scampering of tiny feet, and The Thinking Machine passed into the gloom of the cell. Then the door was closed and double locked by the warden.

"What is that noise in there?" asked Dr. Ransome, through the bars.

"Rats—dozens of them," replied The Thinking Machine, tersely.

The three men, with final good nights, were turning away when The Thinking Machine called: "Exactly, what time is it now, warden?"

"Eleven seventeen," replied the warden.

"Thank you. I will join you gentlemen in your office at half-past eight o'clock one week from tonight," said The Thinking Machine.

"And if you do not?"

"There is no 'if' about it."

Chisholm Prison was a great, spreading structure of granite, four stories high, which stood in the center of acres of open space. It was surrounded by a stone wall eighteen feet high, so smoothly finished as to offer no foothold to a climber. Even if a man could escape from his cell, it would be impossible for him to climb the wall.

At all times of the day there were armed guards in the yard, four of them, one patrolling each side of the prison building. At night the yard was almost as brilliantly lighted as by day. On each of the four sides a great arc light rose above the prison wall and gave the guards a clear view. The wires which fed the arc lights ran up the side of the prison building on insulators. From the top story these wires led out to the poles supporting the arc lights.

All these things were noted by The Thinking Ma-

chine, who could see out of his closely barred cell window by standing on his bed. This was on the morning after he had been locked in the cell. He gathered, too, that the river lay somewhere beyond the wall, because he heard faintly the droning of a motorboat and high up in the air saw a river bird. From that same direction came the shouts of boys at play and the occasional crack of a batted ball. He knew, then, that between the prison wall and the river was an open space, a playground.

Chisholm Prison was regarded as absolutely safe. No man had ever escaped from it. The Thinking Machine, from his perch on the bed, noting what he saw, could readily understand why. The walls of the cell were perfectly solid, and the window bars of new iron had not a shadow of rust on them. The window itself, even with the bars removed, would be a difficult way out because it was small.

Yet, The Thinking Machine was not discouraged. Instead, he squinted thoughtfully at the great arc light—there was bright sunlight now—and traced with his eyes the wire which led to the building. That electric wire, he reasoned, must come down the side of the building not a great distance from his cell. *That might be worth noting.*

Cell 13 was on the same floor as the offices of the prison—that is, not in the basement, nor was it upstairs. There were only four steps up to the office floor. Therefore the level of the floor must be only three or four feet above the ground. The Professor could not see the ground directly beneath his window, but he could see it farther out toward the wall. It would be an easy drop from the window. Well and good.

Then, The Thinking Machine fell to remembering how he had come to the cell. First, there was the outside guard's booth, a part of the wall. There were two gates heavily barred, both of steel. At this gate one man was always on guard. This guard admitted persons to the prison with much clanking of keys and locks, and only let them out when ordered to do so. The warden's office was in the prison building. In order to reach that official from the prison yard one had to pass a gate of solid steel with only a peephole in it. Then, coming from that inner office to his Cell 13, one must pass a heavy wooden door and two steel doors into the corridors of the prison; and always there was the double-locked door of Cell 13 to reckon with.

There were then, The Thinking Machine recalled, seven doors to reckon with before one could pass from Cell 13 into the outer world, a free man. But against this obstacle was the fact he was rarely interrupted. A jailer appeared at his cell door at six in the morning with a breakfast of prison fare; he would come again at noon, and again at six in the afternoon. At nine o'clock at night would come the inspection tour. That would be all.

There was nothing, positively nothing, in his cell,

except his iron bed, and this was so firmly put together that no man could take it apart except with sledges or a file. The Professor had neither of these. There was not even a chair, or a small table, or a bit of tin or crockery. Nothing! The jailer stood by when he ate, then took away the wooden spoon and bowl which he had used.

One by one these things sank into the brain of The Thinking Machine. He began an examination of his cell. From the roof, down the walls on each side, he studied the stones and the cement between them. He stamped on the floor carefully time after time. It was cement, perfectly solid. After this examination he sat on the edge of the iron bed, lost in thought for a long time. Professor Augustus S. F. X. Van Dusen, The Thinking Machine, had something to think about.

He was disturbed by a rat, which ran across his foot, then scampered away into a dark corner of the cell, as if frightened at its own daring. The Thinking Machine squinted steadily into the darkness of the corner where the rat had gone. After awhile he was able to make out in the gloom many little beady eyes staring at him. He counted six pair, and there were perhaps others; he didn't see very well.

Seated on his bed, The Thinking Machine then noticed for the first time the bottom of his cell door. There was an opening of two inches between the steel bar and the floor. Looking steadily at this opening, The Thinking Machine backed suddenly into the corner where he had seen the beady eyes. There was a great scampering of tiny feet, several squeaks of frightened rodents, and then silence.

None of the rats had gone out the door, yet there were none in the cell. *Therefore there must be another way* out of the cell, however small.

The Thinking Machine got down on his hands and knees. Feeling in the darkness with his long, slender fingers, he started a search for this spot.

At last his search was rewarded. He came upon a small opening in the floor, level with the cement. It was perfectly round and somewhat larger than a silver dollar. This was the way the rats had gone. He put his fingers deep into the opening; it seemed to be an unused drainage pipe and was dry and dusty.

Noon came and the jailer appeared with the prison dinner. The Thinking Machine took what was offered without comment. Occasionally he spoke to the jailer who stood outside the door watching him.

"Any improvements made here in the last few years?" he asked.

"Nothing special," replied the jailer. "New wall was built four years ago."

"Anything done to the prison proper?"

"They painted the woodwork outside, and I believe about seven years ago a new system of plumbing was put in."

"Ah!" said the prisoner. "How far is the river over there?"

"About three hundred feet. The boys have a base-ball ground between the wall and the river."

The Thinking Machine had nothing further to say just then, but when the jailer was ready to go, he asked for some water.

"I get very thirsty here," he explained. "Could you leave a little water in a bowl for me?"

"I'll ask the warden," replied the jailer, and he went away.

Half an hour later he returned with water in a small earthen bowl.

"The warden says you may keep this bowl," he informed the prisoner. "But you must show it to me when I ask for it. If it is broken, you won't get another one."

"Thank you," said The Thinking Machine. "I shan't break it."

The jailer went on about his duties. For just the fraction of a second it seemed that The Thinking Machine wanted to ask a question, but he didn't.

Two hours later this same jailer, in passing the door of Cell No. 13, heard a noise inside and stopped. The Thinking Machine was down on his hands and knees in a corner of the cell. From that corner came several frightened squeaks. The jailer looked on with interest.

"Ah, I've got you," he heard the prisoner say.

"Got what?" the jailer asked sharply.

"One of these rats," was the reply. "See?" Between the scientist's long fingers the jailer saw a small

14

gray rat struggling. The prisoner brought it over to the light and looked at it closely. "It's a water rat," he said.

"Take it away and kill it. There are dozens more where it came from."

Still later that afternoon the outside armed guard on the Cell 13 side of the prison looked up again at the window and saw the prisoner looking out. He saw a hand raised to the barred window. Then something white fluttered to the ground, directly under the window of Cell 13. It was a little roll of linen, evidently

of white shirting material, and tied around it was a five-dollar bill. The guard looked up at the window again, but the face had disappeared.

With a smile he took the little linen roll and the five-dollar bill to the warden's office. There together they deciphered some words on the outside of the roll of linen. Written with a queer sort of ink, and frequently blurred was this message:

"Finder of this please deliver to Dr. Charles Ransome."

"Ah," said the warden, with a chuckle. "Plan of escape number one has gone wrong." Then, as an afterthought: "But why did he address it to Dr. Ransome?"

"And where did he get the pen and ink to write with?" asked the guard.

The warden looked at the guard and the guard looked at the warden. There was no easy solution to that mystery. The warden studied the writing carefully, then shook his head.

"Well, let's see what he was going to say to Dr. Ransome," he said at length. Still puzzled, he unrolled the inner piece of linen.

"Well, if that—what—what do you think of that?" he asked, dazed.

The guard took the bit of linen and read this:
Epa cseot d'net niiy awe htto n'si sih. "T."

The warden spent an hour wondering what sort of

code the Professor had used, and half an hour wondering why he should attempt to communicate with Dr. Ransome. After this the warden devoted some thought to the question of where the prisoner had obtained writing materials, and what sort of writing materials he had. The warden examined the piece of linen again. The edges were ragged and he could see that it was a torn part of a white shirt.

But what had the prisoner used to write with? The warden knew it would have been impossible for him to have obtained either pen or pencil. Morever, neither pen nor pencil had been used in this writing. What, then? The warden decided to investigate personally.

The warden went back to Cell 13 and found The Thinking Machine on his hands and knees on the floor, engaged in nothing more alarming than catching rats. The prisoner heard the warden's step and turned to him quickly.

"It's disgraceful," he snapped, "these rats. There are scores of them."

"Other men have been able to stand them," said the warden. "Here is another shirt for you—let me have the one you have on."

"Why?"

"You have tried to contact Dr. Ransome," said the warden severely. "As my prisoner, it is my duty to put a stop to that."

The prisoner arose from the floor and removed the

white shirt, putting on instead the striped convict shirt the warden had brought. The warden took the white shirt eagerly. Then and there he compared the linen on which the code was written with certain torn places in the shirt.

"What did you write this with?" demanded the warden.

"I should think it a part of your duty to find out!"

The warden started to say something harsh, then restrained himself. He made a careful search of the cell and of the prisoner. He found absolutely nothing; not even a match or toothpick which might have been used as a pen. The same mystery surrounded the fluid with which the code had been written. Although the warden left Cell 13 visibly annoyed, he took the torn shirt in triumph.

"Well, writing notes on a shirt won't get him out, that's certain," he told himself as he put the linen scraps into his desk. "If that man escapes from that cell I'll—hang it—I'll resign."

On the third day of his imprisonment, The Thinking Machine openly attempted to bribe his way out. The jailer had brought his dinner and was leaning against the barred door, waiting, when The Thinking Machine began the conversation.

"The drainage pipes of the prison lead to the river, don't they?" he asked.

"Yes," replied the jailer.

"I suppose they are very small?"

"Too small to crawl through, if that's what you're thinking about," the jailer said with a grin.

There was silence until The Thinking Machine finished his meal. Then: "You know I'm not a criminal, don't you?"

"Yes."

"And that I've got a perfect right to be freed if I demand it?"

"Yes."

"Well, I came here believing that I could make my escape," said the prisoner, and his squinting eyes studied the face of the jailer. "Would you consider a financial reward for helping me to escape?"

The jailer, who happened to be an honest man, looked at the slender, weak figure of the prisoner, at the large head with its mass of yellow hair, and was almost sorry.

"Prisons like this were not built for the likes of you to get out of," he said, at last, shaking his head.

"But would you consider a proposition to help me get out?" The Thinking Machine seemed to be pleading.

"No," said the jailer, shortly.

"Five hundred dollars," urged The Thinking Machine. "I am not a criminal, you know."

"No," said the jailer.

"A thousand?"

"No," said the jailer again, and he walked hurriedly to escape further temptation. Then he turned back. "If you should give me ten thousand dollars I couldn't get you out. You'd have to pass through seven doors, and I only have the keys to two."

The jailer went directly to the warden and told him of the Professor's offer.

"Plan number two fails," said the warden, smiling grimly. "First a code, then bribery."

At six o'clock the jailer was on his way to Cell 13 with food for The Thinking Machine. He paused and listened intently. For he heard the unmistakable scrape, scrape of steel against steel. It stopped at the sound of his steps.

After a moment he heard it again—the steady scrape, scrape, and the jailer crept cautiously on tiptoe to the door and peered between the bars. The Thinking Machine was standing on the iron bed working at the bars of the little window. He was using a file, judging from the backward and forward swing of his arms.

Cautiously the jailer went back to the office and summoned the warden. The two men returned to Cell 13 on tiptoe. The steady scrape was still audible. The warden listened to satisfy himself. Then suddenly he appeared at the door.

"Well?" he demanded, and there was a triumphant smile on his face.

The Thinking Machine leaped suddenly from his perch on the bed and made frantic efforts to hide something. The warden went in, his hand extended.

"Give it up," he said.

"No," said the prisoner, sharply.

"Come, give it up," urged the warden. "I don't want to have to search you again."

"No," repeated the prisoner.

"What was it, a file?" asked the warden.

The Thinking Machine was silent and stood squinting at the warden with something close to disappointment on his face. The warden was almost sympathetic.

21

"Plan number three fails, eh?" he asked, good-naturedly. "Too bad, isn't it?"

The prisoner did not answer.

"Search him," instructed the warden.

The jailer searched the prisoner carefully. At last, artfully concealed in the waistband of the trousers, he found a piece of steel about two inches long, with one side curved like a half moon.

"Ah," said the warden, as he received it from the jailer. "From your shoe heel," and he smiled pleasantly.

The jailer continued his search and on the other side of the trousers waistband found another piece of steel that was identical. The edges showed where they had been worn against the bars of the window.

"You couldn't saw a way through those bars with these," said the warden.

"I could have," said The Thinking Machine firmly.

"In six months, perhaps," said the warden, good-naturedly.

The warden shook his head slowly as he gazed into the slightly flushed face of his prisoner.

"Ready to give it up?" he asked.

"I haven't started yet," was the prompt reply.

Then came another search of the cell. Carefully the two men went over it, finally turning out the bed and searching that. They found nothing. The warden himself climbed upon the bed and examined the bars of the window which the prisoner had been sawing. He was amused at what he observed.

"Just made it a little bright by hard rubbing," he said to the prisoner, who stood looking on with a somewhat crestfallen air. The warden grasped the iron bars in his strong hands and tried to shake them. They were immovable, set firmly in the solid granite. He examined each in turn and found them all satisfactory. Finally he climbed down from the bed.

"Give it up, Professor," he advised.

The Thinking Machine shook his head and the warden and jailer left the cell. As they disappeared down the corridor The Thinking Machine sat on the edge of the bed with his head in his hands.

"He's crazy to try to get out of that cell," the jailer commented.

"Of course he can't get out," said the warden. "But he's clever. I would like to know what he wrote with. We searched him carefully. He did not have pen, ink, or pencil when he came here. How did he write the code?"

Four o'clock next morning a strange thing happened. A dreadful scream sounded through the great prison—a shriek of pure terror. It came from a cell, somewhere in the center of the building. The warden rushed with three of his men into the long corridor leading to Cell 13.

As they ran down the corridor they heard it again— an awful cry that died away in a sort of wail. White-faced prisoners appeared at cell doors upstairs and down, staring out wondering, frightened.

"It's that fool in Cell 13," grumbled the warden.

He stopped and stared as one of the jailers flashed a lantern. "That fool in Cell 13" lay comfortably on his cot, flat on his back with his mouth open, snoring. Even as they looked there came again the piercing cry, from somewhere above. The warden's face blanched as he started up the stairs. Directly above Cell 13, on the top floor but two floors higher was Cell 43. There the warden found a prisoner cowering in a corner of his cell.

"What's the matter?" demanded the warden.

"Thank God you've come," cried the prisoner, trembling.

"What is it?" demanded the warden again.

He threw open the door and went in. The prisoner dropped to his knees and clasped the warden about the body. His face was white, his eyes were distended, and he was shuddering. His hands, icy cold, clutched at the warden.

"Take me out of this cell," he begged, "please take me out."

"What's the matter with you, anyhow?" the warden asked impatiently.

"I heard something—something," said the prisoner, and he looked wildly around the cell.

"What did you hear?"

"I—I can't tell you," stammered the prisoner. Then,

in a voice full of terror he cried again, "Take me out of this cell—put me anywhere—but take me out of here."

The warden and the three jailers exchanged glances.

"Who is this fellow? What's he accused of?" asked the warden.

"Joseph Ballard," said one of the jailers. "He's accused of throwing acid in a woman's face."

"They can't prove it," gasped the prisoner. "They can't prove it. Please—please—put me in some other cell."

"Look here, Ballard," said the warden, finally, "if you heard anything, I want to know what it was. Now tell me."

"I can't, I can't," was the reply. The man was sobbing now.

"This sound—where did it come from?"

"I don't know. Everywhere—nowhere. I just heard it."

"What was it—a voice?"

"It was a voice—but—but it wasn't human," was the sobbing reply.

"A voice? Not human?" repeated the warden, puzzled.

"It sounded muffled and—and far away—and ghostly." The man shuddered.

"Did it come from inside or outside the prison?"

"I don't know . . . it was just here, here, there, everywhere. I heard it. I tell you, I heard it!"

The warden went his way, a greatly puzzled man. Ballard sat at his cell door until daylight, his white drawn face pressed against the bars, looking out into the prison with wide, staring eyes.

That day, the fourth since the imprisonment of The Thinking Machine, was enlivened considerably by the volunteer prisoner. He spent most of his time at the little window of his cell. He began by throwing another piece of linen down to the guard, who picked it up dutifully and took it to the warden. On it was written:

"Only three days more."

The warden was in no way surprised at what he read. He understood that The Thinking Machine meant only three days more of his imprisonment, and he regarded the note as a boast. But how was the thing written? Where had The Thinking Machine found this new piece of linen? Where? How? He examined the linen carefully. It was white shirting material of fine texture. He examined the shirt which he had taken from the Professor and carefully fitted the two original pieces of the linen to the torn places. This third piece didn't fit anywhere. Yet it was unmistakably of the same material!

"And where—*where* does he get anything to write with?" the warden asked himself.

Still later on the fourth day The Thinking Machine spoke through the window of his cell to the armed guard outside.

"What day of the month is it?" he asked.

"The fifteenth," was the answer.

The Thinking Machine made a mental astronomical calculation and satisfied himself that the moon would not rise until after nine o'clock that night. Then he asked another question: "Who attends to those arc lights?"

"Man from the company."

"You have no electricians in the building?"

"No."

That day the guard noticed that The Thinking Machine was at the cell window frequently. The prisoner seemed listless and after a while the guard accepted his presence there as a matter of course. He had seen other prisoners stand and stare in the same way; it was the longing for the outside world.

That afternoon, just before the day guard was relieved, the Professor's head appeared at the window again. This time his hand held something out between the bars. It fluttered to the ground and the guard picked it up. It was a five-dollar bill.

"That's for you," called the prisoner.

As usual, the guard took the money to the warden. That gentleman looked at it suspiciously; he now looked at everything that came from Cell 13 with suspicion.

"He said it was for me," explained the guard.

"It's a sort of a tip, I suppose," said the warden. "I see no particular reason why you shouldn't accept—"

Suddenly he stopped. He had remembered that The Thinking Machine had gone into Cell 13 with one five-dollar bill and two ten-dollar bills; twenty-five dollars in all. A five-dollar bill had been tied around the first piece of linen that came from the cell. The warden still had that bill. To convince himself he took it out and looked at it. Yes, it was five dollars. The Thinking Machine had only had ten-dollar bills. Yet here was another five-dollar bill!

"Perhaps somebody changed one of the bills for him," the warden thought at last, with a sigh of relief.

But then and there he made up his mind. He would search Cell 13 as a cell had never been searched before. When a prisoner could write at will, change money, and do other wholly inexplicable things, something was wrong with his prison. The warden planned to enter the cell at night—three o'clock would be an excellent time. The Thinking Machine must do all the weird things he did sometime. Night seemed the most reasonable.

The warden descended stealthily upon Cell 13 that night at three o'clock. He paused at the door and listened. There was no sound save the steady, regular breathing of the prisoner. The keys unfastened the double locks with scarcely a clank, and the warden entered, locking the door behind him.

If the warden had planned to startle The Thinking Machine he was disappointed. The scientist merely opened his eyes quietly, reached for his glasses and inquired, in a matter-of-fact tone: "Who is it?"

It would be useless to describe the search that the warden made. Not one inch of the cell or the bed was overlooked. He found the round hole in the floor, and thrust his thick fingers into it. After a moment of fumbling there he drew up something and looked at it in the light of his lantern.

The thing he had taken out was a rat—a dead rat. He continued the search. The Thinking Machine, without a word, arose and kicked the rat out of the cell into the corridor.

The warden climbed on the bed and tried the steel bars in the tiny window. They were perfectly rigid; every bar of the door was secure.

Then the warden searched the prisoner's clothing, beginning at the shoes. Nothing hidden in them! Then the trousers waistband. Still nothing! Then the pockets of the trousers. From one side he drew out some paper money and examined it.

"Five one-dollar bills," he gasped.

"That's right," said the prisoner.

"But the—you had two tens and a five—what the—how do you do it?"

"That's my business," said The Thinking Machine.

"Did any of my men change this money for you—on your word of honor?"

The Thinking Machine paused just a fraction of a second.

"No," he said.

"Well, do you make it?" asked the warden. He was prepared to believe anything.

"That's my business," again replied the prisoner.

The warden glared at the eminent scientist. He felt —he knew—that this man was making a fool of him, yet he didn't know how. Neither of the men spoke for some time. Then the warden turned abruptly and left the cell, slamming the door behind him. He did not trust himself to speak.

It was ten minutes to four before the warden, weary and baffled, got into bed. And he had hardly settled himself in bed when once more that shriek rang through the prison. The warden lighted his lantern and rushed through the prison again to the cell on the upper floor.

Again the prisoner Ballard was crushed against the steel door, shrieking—shrieking at the top of his voice. He stopped only when the warden flashed his lamp in the cell.

"Take me out, take me out," he screamed. "I did it, I did it, I— Take it away."

"Take what away?" asked the warden.

"I threw the acid in her face—I did it—I confess. Take me out of here."

Ballard's condition was pitiable; it was only an act of mercy to let him out into the corridor. There he crouched in a corner, like an animal at bay, clasping his hands to his ears. It took half an hour to calm him sufficiently so he could speak. Then he told incoherently what had happened. He had heard that voice again, muffled and wailing.

"What did it say?" asked the warden.

"Acid—acid—acid!" gasped the prisoner. "It accused me. Acid! I threw the acid, I did it! Oh!" It was a long, shuddering wail of terror.

"Acid?" echoed the warden.

"Acid. That's all I heard—that one word, again and again. There was more, too, but I didn't understand it."

"That was last night, eh?" asked the warden. "What happened tonight—what frightened you just now?"

"The same thing," gasped the prisoner. "Acid—acid—acid!" He covered his face with his hands. "It was acid I used on her, but I didn't mean to kill her."

"Did you hear anything else?"

"Yes—but I couldn't understand—just a word or two."

"Well, what was it?"

"I heard 'acid' three times, then I heard a long, moaning sound, then—then—I heard 'Number 8 hat.' I heard that twice."

"Number 8 hat," repeated the warden. "What the devil—Number 8 hat?" Accusing voices of conscience had never before talked about Number 8 hats, so far as the warden knew.

"He's insane," said one of the jailers.

"I believe you," said the warden. "He must be. But

31

he certainly heard something that frightened him. He's
trembling all over. Number 8 hat! What the—"

When the fifth day of The Thinking Machine's imprisonment rolled around the warden was wearing a
hunted look. He was anxious for the end of the experiment. He could not help but feel that his distinguished prisoner had been amusing himself. If this
were so, The Thinking Machine had lost none of his
sense of humor. For on this fifth day he threw another
linen note to the outside guard, bearing the words:
"Only two days more." This time he also flung down
half a dollar.

Now the warden knew—he *knew*—that the man in
Cell 13 didn't have any half dollars— He *couldn't*
have any half dollars, any more than he could have
pen and ink and linen. And yet he *DID* have them.
That is one reason why the warden wore a hunted
look.

That uncanny business about "Acid" and "Number 8
hat" bothered him, too. It couldn't mean anything, of
course, merely the ravings of an insane man who had
been driven by fear to confess his crime. Still too
many things that "didn't mean anything" were happening in the prison now that The Thinking Machine
was there.

On the sixth day the warden received a letter stating
that Dr. Ransome and Mr. Fielding would be at Chisholm Prison on the following evening, Thursday. In

the event Professor Van Dusen had not yet escaped—and they presumed he had not because they had not heard from him—they would meet him there.

"In the event he had not yet escaped!" The warden smiled grimly. Escaped!

The Thinking Machine enlivened this day for the warden with three notes. They were on the usual linen and bore generally on the appointment at half-past eight o'clock Thursday night, the appointment the scientist had made at the time of his imprisonment.

On the afternoon of the seventh day the warden passed Cell 13 and glanced in. The Thinking Machine was lying on the iron bed, apparently sleeping lightly. The cell looked to him precisely as it always did. It was then four o'clock. The warden would swear that no man was going to leave Cell 13 in the next four hours.

On his way back past the cell the warden heard the steady breathing again. Coming close to the door, he looked in.

A ray of light coming through the high window fell on the face of the sleeping man. It occurred to the warden for the first time that his prisoner appeared haggard and weary. At that moment the Professor stirred slightly and the warden hurried up the corridor guiltily.

That evening after six o'clock he saw the jailer.

"Everything all right in Cell 13?" he asked.

"Yes, sir," replied the jailer. "He didn't eat much, though."

It was with a feeling of having done his duty that the warden received Dr. Ransome and Mr. Fielding shortly after seven o'clock. He intended to show them the linen notes and lay before them the full story of his woes. Before he could begin, the guard from the river side of the prison yard entered the office.

"The arc light on my side of the yard won't light," the guard reported to the warden.

"Confound it, that man's a hoodoo," thundered the warden. "Everything has happened since he's been here."

The guard went back to his post in the darkness, and the warden phoned the electric light company.

"This is Chisholm Prison," he said through the phone. "Send three or four men down here at once, to fix an arc light."

The reply was evidently satisfactory, for the warden hung up the receiver and went into the yard. While Dr. Ransome and Mr. Fielding sat waiting, the guard at the outer gate came in with a special delivery letter. Dr. Ransome happened to notice the address. When the guard went out, he looked at the letter more closely.

"By George!" he exclaimed.

"What is it?" asked Mr. Fielding.

Silently the doctor offered the letter. Mr. Fielding examined it closely.

"Coincidence," he said firmly. "It must be."

It was nearly eight o'clock when the warden returned to his office. The electricians had arrived in a wagon, and were now at work. The warden pressed the buzz-button communicating with the man at the outer gate in the wall.

"How many electricians came in?" he asked, over the short phone. "Four? Three workmen in jumpers and overalls and the manager? Frock coat and silk hat? All right. Be certain that only four go out. That's all."

He turned to Dr. Ransome and Mr. Fielding. "We have to be careful here—particularly since we have scientists locked up."

The warden noticed the special delivery letter on his desk. As he ripped open the envelope, he said, "Gentlemen I want to report to you something about how— Great Caesar!" he ended, suddenly, as he read the letter. He sat open-mouthed, motionless, with astonishment.

"What is it?" asked Mr. Fielding.

"A special delivery letter from Cell 13," gasped the warden. "An invitation to supper."

"What?" The other two arose, incredulous.

The warden stared at the letter as if hypnotized. Then he called sharply to a guard outside in the corridor.

"Run down to Cell 13 and see if that man's in there."

The guard left at once. Then Dr. Ransome and Mr. Fielding examined the letter.

"It's the Professor's handwriting; there's no question of that," said Dr. Ransome. "I've seen too much of it."

Just then the buzz sounded on the telephone from the outer gate, and the warden, still dazed, picked up the receiver.

"Hello! Two reporters, eh? Let 'em come in." He turned suddenly to the doctor and Mr. Fielding. "The man *can't* be out. It isn't possible. He *must* be in his cell."

At that moment the guard returned.

"He's still in his cell, sir," he reported. "I saw him. He's lying down."

"There, I told you so," said the warden. He drew a deep breath. "But how did he mail that letter?"

There was a rap on the steel door which led from the jail yard into the warden's office.

"It's the reporters," said the warden. "Let them in," he instructed the guard, then to the two other gentlemen: "Don't say anything about this before them. I'd never hear the last of it!"

The door opened, and two men entered.

"Good-evening, gentlemen," said one of the newcomers. His name was Hutchinson Hatch; the warden knew him well.

"Well?" demanded the other man irritably. "I'm here."

It was The Thinking Machine!

He squinted belligerently at the warden, who sat

down as if his legs had collapsed under him. He was incapable of speech. Dr. Ransome and Mr. Fielding were amazed too, but they didn't know what the warden knew. They were merely astonished, the warden was paralyzed! Hutchinson Hatch, the reporter, took in the scene with amusement.

"How—how—how did you do it?" the warden finally managed to gasp.

"Come back to the cell," said The Thinking Machine.

The warden, in a condition bordering on trance, led the way.

"Flash your light in there," directed the Professor.

The warden did so. There was nothing unusual in the appearance of the cell, and there—there on the bed lay the figure of The Thinking Machine. Certainly! There was the yellow hair! Again the warden looked at the man beside him and wondered if he could be dreaming.

With trembling hands, he unlocked the cell door and The Thinking Machine entered.

"See here," he said.

He kicked at the steel bars in the bottom of the cell door and three of them were pushed out of place. A fourth bar broke off and rolled away in the corridor.

"And here, too," directed the prisoner as he stood on the bed to reach the small window. He swept his hand across the opening and every bar came out.

"What's this in the bed?" demanded the warden, who was slowly recovering.

"A wig," was the reply. "Turn down the cover."

The warden did so. Beneath the cover lay a large coil of strong rope, thirty feet or more, a dagger, three files, ten feet of electric wire, a thin, powerful pair of steel pliers, a small tack hammer with its handle, and—and a pistol.

"How did you do it?" demanded the warden.

"You gentlemen have an engagement for supper with me at half-past eight o'clock," said The Thinking Machine. "Come on, or we shall be late."

"But how did you do it?" the warden insisted.

"Don't ever think you can hold any man who can use his brain," said The Thinking Machine. "Come on; we shall be late."

It was an impatient supper party in the rooms of Professor Van Dusen and a somewhat silent one. The guests were Dr. Ransome, Albert Fielding, the warden, and Hutchinson Hatch, the reporter. The meal was served to the minute, in accordance with Professor Van Dusen's instructions which were given one week before. At last the supper was finished and The Thinking Machine turned to Dr. Ransome.

"Do you believe it now?" he demanded.

"I do," replied Dr. Ransome.

"Do you admit that it was a fair test?"

"I do."

"Suppose you tell us how . . ." began Mr. Fielding. The Thinking Machine began the story. He told it

from the beginning, and no man ever talked to more interested listeners.

"My agreement was," he began, "to go into a cell, carrying nothing except essential clothing, and to leave that cell within a week. I had never seen Chisholm Prison. When I went into the cell I asked for tooth powder, two ten and one five-dollar bills, and to have my shoes polished. Even if these requests had been refused it would not have mattered seriously. But you agreed to them.

"I knew there would be nothing in the cell which

you thought I might use. So when the warden locked the door to my cell I was apparently helpless.

"I was aroused next morning at six o'clock by the jailer with my breakfast," continued the scientist. "He told me dinner was at twelve, and supper at six. Between these times, I gathered, I would be left pretty much to myself. So immediately after breakfast I examined the outside surroundings from my cell window. One look told me it would be useless to try to scale the wall.

"From this first observation I knew the river was on this side of the prison, and that there was also a playground. I knew then one important thing—that anyone might approach the prison wall from this side, if necessary, without attracting any particular attention. That was well to remember. I remembered it.

"But the outside thing which attracted my attention was the feed wire to the arc light which ran within a few feet—probably three or four—of my cell window. I knew that would be valuable in the event I found it necessary to cut off that arc light."

"Oh, you shut it off tonight, then?" asked the warden.

"Having learned all I could from that window," The Thinking Machine went on, without heeding the interruption, "I considered the idea of escaping through the prison proper. I recalled just how I had come into the cell, which I knew would be the only way. Seven doors lay between me and the outside.

So, for the time being, I gave up the idea of escaping that way. And I couldn't go through the solid granite walls of the cell."

The Thinking Machine paused for a moment. For several minutes there was silence, then the scientist went on:

"While I was thinking about these things a rat ran across my foot. It suggested a new line of thought. There were at least half a dozen rats in the cell—I could see their beady eyes. Yet I had noticed none come under the cell door. I frightened them purposely and watched the cell door to see if they went out that way. They did not, but they were gone. Obviously they went another way. Another way meant another opening.

"I searched for this opening and found it. It was an old drain pipe, long unused and partly choked with dirt and dust. But this was the way the rats had come. They came from somewhere. Where? Drain pipes usually lead outside the prison grounds. This one probably led to the river, or near it. The rats must, therefore, come from that direction.

"When the jailer came with my luncheon he told me two important things, although he didn't know it. One was that a new system of plumbing had been put in the prison seven years before; another that the river was only three hundred feet away. Then I knew positively that the pipe was a part of an old system; I knew, too, that it slanted generally toward the river.

"The first thing was to make the warden think I was trying to communicate with you, Dr. Ransome. So I wrote a note on a piece of linen I tore from my shirt, addressed it to Dr. Ransome, tied a five-dollar bill around it and threw it out the window. I knew the guard would take it to the warden. Have you that first linen note, warden?"

The warden produced the coded message.

"What the deuce does it mean, anyhow?" he asked.

"Read it backward, beginning with the 'T' signature and disregard the division into words," instructed The Thinking Machine.

The warden did so.

"T-h-i-s, this," he spelled, studied it a moment, then read it off, grinning: "This is not the way I intend to escape."

"What did you write it with?" asked Dr. Ransome, after he had examined the linen and passed it to Mr. Fielding.

"This," said The Thinking Machine, and he extended his foot. On it was the shoe he had worn in prison, though the polish was gone—scraped off clean. "The shoe blacking, moistened with water, was my ink; the metal tip of the shoe lace made a fairly good pen."

"You're a wonder," said the warden, admiringly. "Go on."

"That set off a search of my cell by the warden, as I had intended," continued The Thinking Machine. "I

42

was anxious to get the warden into the habit of searching my cell, so that finally, constantly finding nothing,
he would get disgusted and quit.

"Then he took my white shirt away and gave me a
prison shirt. He was satisfied that those two pieces of
the shirt were all that was missing. But while he was
searching my cell I had another piece of that same
shirt, about nine inches square, rolled into a small ball
in my mouth."

"Nine inches of that shirt?" demanded the warden.
"Where did it come from?"

"The bosoms of all stiff white shirts are of triple
thickness," was the explanation. "I tore out the inside
thickness, leaving only two thicknesses. I knew you
wouldn't see it. So much for that.

"Then I took my first serious step toward freedom,"
said Professor Van Dusen. "I knew, within reason, that
the pipe led somewhere to the playground outside;
I knew a great many boys played there; I knew that
rats came into my cell from out there. Could I communicate with some one outside?

"The first thing I needed, I realized, was thread,
so—" he pulled up his trouser legs and showed that
the tops of both stockings woven of strong thread were
gone. "I unraveled those—after I got them started it
wasn't difficult—and I had easily a quarter of a mile
of thread that I could depend on.

"Then on half of the remaining linen I wrote,
laboriously enough I assure you, a letter explaining

43

my situation to this gentleman here," and he indicated Hutchinson Hatch. "I knew he would assist me —for the value of the newspaper story. I tied firmly to this linen letter a ten-dollar bill—there is no surer way of attracting the eye of anyone—and wrote on the linen: 'Finder of this deliver to Hutchinson Hatch, *Daily American,* who will give another ten dollars for the information.'

"The next thing was to get this note outside on that playground where a boy might find it. There were two ways, but I chose the best. I took one of the rats— I became expert in catching them—tied the linen and money firmly to one leg, fastened my thread to another, and turned him loose in the drain pipe. I reasoned that the natural fright of the rodent would make him run until he was outside the pipe and then once outside, he would probably stop to gnaw off the linen and money.

"From the moment the rat disappeared into that dusty pipe I became anxious. I was taking so many chances. The rat might gnaw the string, of which I held one end; other rats might gnaw it; the rat might run out of the pipe and leave the linen and money where they would never be found; a thousand other things might have happened.

"So began some nervous hours, but the fact that the rat ran on until only a few feet of the string remained in my cell made me think he was outside the pipe. I had carefully instructed Mr. Hatch what to do in case the note reached him. The question was: Would it reach him?

"This done, I could only wait and make other plans in case this one failed. I openly attempted to bribe my jailer, and learned from him that he held the keys

to only two of seven doors between me and freedom. Then I did something else to make the warden nervous. I took the steel supports out of the heels of my shoes and made a pretense of sawing the bars of my cell window. The warden raised a pretty row about that. He developed, too, the habit of shaking the bars of my cell window to see if they were solid. They were—then.

"With this one plan I had done all I could and could only wait to see what happened," the scientist went on. "I couldn't know whether my note had been delivered or even found, or whether the rat had gnawed it up. And I didn't dare to draw back through the pipe that one slender thread which connected me with the outside world.

"When I went to bed that night I didn't sleep, for fear there would come the slight signal twitch at the thread which was to tell me that Mr. Hatch had received the note. At half-past three o'clock, I judge, I felt this twitch, and no prisoner ever welcomed a thing more heartily."

The Thinking Machine stopped and turned to the reporter.

"You'd better explain just what you did," he said.

"The linen note was brought to me by a small boy who had been playing baseball," said Mr. Hatch. "I immediately saw a big story in it, so I gave the boy another ten dollars, and got several spools of silk, some twine, and a roll of light, pliable wire. The professor's note suggested that I have the finder of the note show me just where it was picked up, and told me to make my search from there. If I found the other end of the thread I was to twitch it gently three times, then a fourth.

"I began the search with a small electric light bulb.

It was an hour and twenty minutes before I found the end of the drain pipe, half hidden in weeds. The pipe was very large there, about twelve inches across. Then I found the end of the thread, twitched it as directed, and immediately I got an answering twitch.

"Then I fastened the silk to the thread and Professor Van Dusen began to pull it into his cell. I worried a bit for fear the string would break. To the end of the silk I fastened the twine, and when that had been pulled in I tied on the wire. Then that was drawn into the pipe and we had a substantial line, which rats couldn't gnaw, from the mouth of the drain into the cell."

The Thinking Machine raised his hand and Hatch stopped.

"All this was done in absolute silence," said the scientist. "But when the wire reached my hand I could have shouted. Then we tried another experiment, which Mr. Hatch was prepared for. I tested the pipe as a speaking tube. Neither of us could hear very clearly, but I dared not speak loud for fear of attracting attention in the prison. At last I made him understand what I wanted immediately. He seemed to have great difficulty in understanding when I asked for nitric acid, and I repeated the word 'acid' several times.

"Then I heard a shriek from a cell above me. I knew instantly that someone had overheard. If you had entered my cell at that moment, warden, that whole plan of escape would have ended there. But you bypassed my cell. That was the nearest I ever came to being caught.

"It is easy to see how I got things in the cell and made them disappear at will. I merely dropped them back into the pipe. You, warden, could not have reached the connecting wire with your fingers; they are too large. My fingers, you see, are longer and more slender. In addition I guarded the top of that pipe with a rat—you remember how."

"I remember," said the warden.

"I thought that if any one were tempted to investigate that hole the rat would dampen his ardor. Mr. Hatch could not send me anything useful through the pipe until the next night, although he did send me change for ten dollars as a test, so I proceeded with other parts of my plan. Then I planned the method of escape, which I finally used.

"In order to carry this out successfully it was necessary for the guard in the yard to see me at the cell window often. I arranged this by dropping linen notes to him, boastful in tone, to make the warden believe, if possible, one of his assistants was communicating with the outside for me. I would stand at my window for hours gazing out, so the guard could see. Occasionally I spoke to him. In that way I learned that the prison had no electricians of its own, but was dependent upon the lighting company if anything should go wrong.

"That cleared the way to freedom perfectly. Early in the evening of the last day of my imprisonment, when it was dark, I planned to cut the feed wire which was only a few feet from my window, reaching it with an acid-tipped wire I had. That would make that side of the prison perfectly dark while the electricians were searching for the break. That would also bring Mr. Hatch into the prison yard.

"There was only one more thing to do before I actually began the work of setting myself free. This was to arrange final details with Mr. Hatch through our speaking tube. I did this within half an hour after the warden left my cell on the fourth night of my imprisonment. Mr. Hatch again had serious difficulty in understanding me, and I repeated the word 'acid' to him several times, and later the words: 'Number eight hat'—that's my size—and these were the things which made a prisoner upstairs confess, so one of the jailers told me next day. This prisoner heard our voices, confused of course, through the pipe, which also extended to his cell.

"The actual work of cutting the steel bars of the window and door was comparatively easy with nitric acid, which I got through the pipe in thin bottles, but it took time. Hour after hour on the fifth, and sixth, and seventh day, the guard below was looking at me as I worked on the bars of the window with the acid on a piece of wire. I used the tooth powder to prevent the acid spreading. I looked away as I worked and each minute the acid cut deeper into the metal. I noticed that the jailers always tried the door by shaking the *upper part* of the bars, never the lower ones. So I cut the lower bars, leaving them hanging in place by thin strips of metal."

The Thinking Machine sat silent for several minutes.

"I think that makes everything clear," he went on. "Whatever points I have not explained were merely to confuse the warden and jailers. Those things in my bed I brought in to please Mr. Hatch, who wanted to improve the story. Of course, the wig was necessary in my plan. The special delivery letter I wrote and directed in my cell with Mr. Hatch's fountain pen, then sent it out to him and he mailed it. That's all, I think."

"But your actually leaving the prison grounds and then coming in through the outer gate to my office?" asked the warden.

"Perfectly simple," said the scientist. "I cut the electric light wire with acid, as I said, when the current was turned off. Therefore, when the current was turned on, the arc didn't light. I knew it would take some time to find out what the trouble was and make repairs. When the guard went to report to you the yard was dark, I crept out the window—it was a tight fit, too—replaced the bars by standing on a narrow ledge and remained in the shadow until the electricians arrived. Mr. Hatch was one of them.

"When I saw him I spoke and he handed me a cap,

a jumper and overalls, which I put on within ten feet of you, warden, while you were in the yard. Later Mr. Hatch called me, presumably as a workman, and together we went out the gate to get something out of the wagon. The gate guard let us pass out readily as two workmen who had just gone in. We changed our clothing and reappeared, asking to see you. We saw you. That's all."

There was silence for several minutes. Dr. Ransome was first to speak.

"Wonderful!" he exclaimed. "Perfectly amazing."

"How did Mr. Hatch happen to come with the electricians?" asked Mr. Fielding.

"His father is manager of the company," replied The Thinking Machine.

"But what if there had been no Mr. Hatch outside to help?"

"Every prisoner has one friend outside who would help him escape if he could."

"Suppose—just suppose—there had been no old plumbing system there?" asked the warden, curiously.

"There were two other ways out!" said The Thinking Machine, with a puzzling smile.

The Case

of the

Flaming Phantom

AFRAID of ghosts?" asked the City Editor of the
Daily American.

"Don't know," Reporter Hutchinson Hatch replied, smiling a little. "I never happened to meet one."

"Well, this looks like a good story," the City Editor
explained. "It's a haunted house. Nobody can live in
it; all sorts of strange happenings, crazy laughter . . .
groans and things. House is owned by Ernest Weston,
a broker. Better jump down and take a look at it. If
it is promising, you might spend a night in it for a
Sunday story. Not afraid, are you?"

"I never heard of a ghost hurting anyone," Hatch

replied, still smiling. "If this one hurts me, it will make the story better."

Within two hours Hatch was at the old Weston house. It was a two-story, solidly-built frame structure that had been put up sixty or seventy years ago upon a cliff overlooking the sea. The house stood in the center of a plot of land of some ten or twelve acres.

Hatch did not stop to question anyone in the village. Instead, he climbed the steep cliff road to the old house, hoping to find some one who might grant him permission to inspect it. But no one appeared. The house lay deep in gloom. All the shutters were closed forbiddingly.

There was no answer to Hatch's vigorous knock on the front door. He shook the shutters on a window without result. Then he went around to the back of the house. Here Hatch found a door. He hammered on it, but still there was no answer. He tried the door, and finding it open, walked in. He now stood in the kitchen of the old house, a damp room, chilly and darkened by the closed shutters.

Hatch glanced about this room briefly, and went on through a back hall to the dining room. Here the hardwood floor was covered with dust. There was no furniture, only litter.

From this point, just inside the dining room door, Hatch began a sort of study of the inside architecture of the house. To his left was a door—the butler's

pantry. There was a passage through, down three steps into the kitchen he had just left.

Straight before him, set in the wall, between two windows, was a large mirror, seven, possibly eight, feet tall and proportionately wide. A mirror of the same size was set in the wall at the end of the room to his left.

From the dining room he passed through a wide archway into the next room. This archway made the two rooms almost as one. The second room, he presumed, had been a sort of living room, but here, too, there was nothing but litter, an old-fashioned fireplace and two long mirrors. As he entered the room, the fireplace was to his immediate left; one of the large mirrors was straight ahead of him and the other was to his right.

Next to the mirror at the end was a passageway which had once been closed with a sliding door. Hatch went through this into the reception hall of the old house. Here, to his right, was the main hall, connected with the reception hall by an archway, and through this archway he could see a wide, old-fashioned stairway leading to an upper story. To his left was a door, of ordinary size, closed. He tried this door and found it unlocked. Hatch peered into the big room beyond. This room had been the library. It smelled of books and damp wood. There was nothing here—not even mirrors.

As the reporter passed through room after room he

fixed the general arrangement of the house in his mind.

After another examination of the lower floor, Hatch went out the back way to the barn. This stood a few hundred feet behind the house. In the upper part of the barn, reached by outside stairs, were apartments intended for the servants. Hatch found that these rooms, too, had the appearance of not having been occupied for several years. The lower part of the barn, he noted, was arranged to house half a dozen horses.

"Nothing here to frighten anybody," he thought as he started back toward the village. It was three o'clock in the afternoon. His purpose now was to learn all he could about the "ghost," and to return to the house that night.

He sought out the town constable, a grizzled old fellow of sixty years, who had the gossip and information of several generations at the tip of his tongue.

The old man talked happily for two hours. He seemed to have been longing for just such a glorious opportunity as the reporter offered.

According to the constable, the Weston house had not been occupied for five years—not since the death of the father of Ernest Weston, the present owner. Then, just two weeks ago, Ernest Weston had come down with a contractor and looked over the old place.

"We had heard," said the constable, "that Mr. Weston is going to be married soon, and we kind of thought he was having the house made ready for his summer home again."

"Do you know whom he is to marry?" asked Hatch, for this was news indeed.

"Miss Katherine Everard, daughter of Curtis Everard, a banker up in Boston," was the reply. "I know Mr. Weston used to go around with her before the old man died, and they say since he met her in Newport he has spent a lot of time with her."

"Oh, I see," said Hatch. "They were to marry and come here to live?"

"That's right," said the constable. "But I don't know what will happen now that this ghost story has come up."

"What is the story, anyway?"

"Well," and the old constable rubbed his chin thoughtfully, "it does seem kind of funny. I never heard of a ghost there before. The trouble began a few days after Mr. Weston was here. A gang of laborers came down to work and decided to sleep in the house—sort of camp out—until they could repair a leak in the barn and move in there. They got here late in the afternoon and didn't do much that day but move into the house, to the upstairs part, and sort of settle down for the night. About one o'clock they heard some sort of noise downstairs, and finally all kinds of racket and groans and yells, and they just naturally came down to see what it was.

"Then they saw the ghost. It was in the reception hall, some of 'em said. Others said it was in the library. But anyhow it was there, and the whole gang left just as fast as they knew how. They slept on the ground that night. Next day they took out their things and went back to Boston. Since then nobody here has heard from 'em."

"What sort of a ghost was it?"

"Oh, it was a tall ghost, about nine feet high, and it was blazing from head to foot as if it was burning up," said the constable. "It had a long knife in its hand and waved it at 'em. They didn't stop to argue. They ran, and as they ran, they heard the ghost a-laughing at them."

"I should think it would have been amused," was Hatch's comment. "Has anybody who lives in the village seen the ghost?"

"No; we're willing enough to take their word for it," the constable replied. "I do go up and look the place over every afternoon, and everything seems to be all right, but I haven't gone there at night. It's quite a way off my beat," he hastened to explain.

"A tall ghost with a long knife," mused Hatch. "Seems to be burning up, eh? That sounds exciting. Now, a ghost who knows its business never appears except where there has been a murder. Was there ever a murder in that house?"

"When I was a youngster, I heard there was a murder or something there; but I suppose if I don't remember it, nobody else here does," was the old man's reply. "It happened one winter when the Westons weren't there. There was something, too, about jewelry

59

and diamonds, but I don't remember just what it was."

"Indeed!"

"Yes, something about somebody trying to steal a lot of jewelry—maybe a hundred thousand dollars' worth. Nobody ever paid much attention to it. I just heard about it when I was a boy, and that was more'n fifty years ago."

"I see," said the reporter.

That night at nine o'clock, under cover of darkness, Hatch climbed the cliff toward the Weston house.

At one o'clock he came racing down the hill, with frequent glances over his shoulder. His face was pale with a fear which he had never known before. Once in his room in the village hotel he lighted a lamp with trembling hands and sat with side, staring eyes until the dawn broke.

HE HAD SEEN THE FLAMING PHANTOM!

It was ten o'clock that morning when Hutchinson Hatch called on Professor Augustus S. F. X. Van Dusen—The Thinking Machine.

"I've been frightened," he said with a sheepish grin; "horribly, awfully frightened. I came to you to find out what frightened me."

"Very interesting, very interesting," said The Thinking Machine. "Go on, please."

Then Hatch told him from the beginning the story

of the haunted house as he knew it; how he had examined the house by daylight, just what he had found, the rumors of an old murder . . . of precious jewels, and the fact that Ernest Weston was to be married. The scientist listened attentively.

"It was nine o'clock that night when I went to the house the second time," said Hatch. "I went prepared for something, but not for what I saw."

"And what was it that you saw?" asked The Thinking Machine.

"I went in while it was perfectly dark. I took a position on the stairs because I had been told the—the THING—had been seen from the stairs, and I thought that where it had been seen once it would be seen again. I had presumed it was some trick of a shadow, or moonlight, or something of the kind. So I sat waiting calmly. I am not a nervous man—that is, I never have been until now.

"I took no light of any kind with me. Hours went by as I waited, staring into the reception room in the general direction of the library. At last, as I gazed into the darkness, I heard a noise. It startled me a bit, but it didn't frighten me. I thought it might be a rat running across the floor.

"But after awhile I heard the most awful cry a human being ever listened to. It was neither a moan nor a shriek—it was merely a—a cry. Then, as I steadied my nerves a little, a figure—a blazing, burning white figure—emerged out of nothingness before my very eyes, in the reception room. It actually emerged in a somewhat human shape as I looked at it!

"The thing was, I should say, about eight feet high. Don't think I'm a fool—I'm not exaggerating. It was all in white and seemed to radiate a light—a ghostly, unearthly light, which, as I looked, grew brighter. There was no face to the THING, but it had a head. Then I saw an arm raised and in the hand was a dagger, blazing as the figure was.

"By this time, I assure you, I was a cringing, frightened coward. And then, even as I looked, the—the THING—raised the other hand, and there, in the air before my eyes, wrote with his own finger—*on the very face of the air,* mind you—one word: 'Beware!' "

"Was it a man's or woman's writing?" asked The Thinking Machine.

The matter-of-fact tone steadied Hatch, who was beginning to tremble a little. He laughed nervously.

"I don't know," he said. "I don't know."

"Go on."

"I have never considered myself a coward, and certainly I am not a fool to be frightened at a thing which my reason tells me is not possible. Despite my fright, I compelled myself to action. If the THING were a man I was not afraid of it, dagger and all; if it were not, it could do me no injury.

"I leaped down the three steps to the bottom of the stairs, and while the THING stood there with up-raised dagger, with one hand pointing at me, I rushed

for it. I think I must have shouted, because I have a dim idea that I heard my own voice. But whether or not I did, I . . ."

Again he paused. It was a distinct effort to pull himself together. He felt like a fool, with the cold, squinting eyes of The Thinking Machine watching him so attentively.

"Then . . . just as it seemed I had my hands on it the THING disappeared! I was expecting a dagger thrust. But while I was staring at it, it started to disappear before my eyes; I suddenly saw *only half of it*. Again I heard the cry, and the other half disappeared —my hands grasped empty air.

"Where the THING had been there was nothing! The impetus of my rush was such that I went right on past the spot where the THING had been, and found myself groping in the dark in a room which I didn't place for an instant. Now I remember it was the library.

"By this time I was half mad with terror. I smashed one of the windows and went through it. From there, until I reached my room, I didn't stop running. I couldn't. I wouldn't have gone back to the reception room for all the millions in the world."

The Thinking Machine twiddled his fingers idly; Hatch sat gazing at him with anxious, eager inquiry in his eyes.

"So when you ran and the . . . the THING moved

away or disappeared, you found yourself in the library?" The Thinking Machine asked at last.

"Yes."

"Therefore, you must have run from the reception room through the library?"

"Yes."

"You left the door closed that day?"

"Yes."

Again there was a pause.

"Did you smell anything?" asked the Thinking Machine.

"No."

"You figure that the THING, as you call it, must have been just about in the doorway?"

"Yes."

"Too bad you didn't notice the handwriting—that is, whether it seemed to be a man's or a woman's."

"I think, under the circumstances, I would be excused for omitting that," Hatch said drily.

"You said you heard something that you thought must be a rat," went on The Thinking Machine. "What was this?"

"I don't know."

"Did it squeak at all?"

"Not that I remember."

"Five years since the house was occupied," mused the scientist. "How far away is the water?"

"The place overlooks the water, but it's a steep

climb of three hundred yards from the water to the house."

That seemed to satisfy The Thinking Machine.

"When you went over the house in daylight, did you notice if any of the mirrors were dusty?" he asked.

"I should presume that all were," was the reply. "There's no reason why they should have been otherwise."

"But you didn't notice particularly that some were not dusty?" the scientist insisted.

"No. I merely noticed that they were there."

The Thinking Machine sat for a long time squinting at the ceiling, then asked, abruptly: "Have you seen Mr. Weston, the owner?"

"No."

"See him and find out what he has to say about the place, the rumors of the murder, the jewels, and all that. Wouldn't it be strange if, say, a fortune in jewels should be hidden somewhere about the place?"

"It would," said Hatch. "It most certainly would."

"Oh, by the way," The Thinking Machine added, "look up something of the family history of the Westons. How many heirs were there? Who are they? How much did each one get?"

Hatch left, far more composed than when he had arrived, and began the work of getting the information The Thinking Machine had asked for.

Hatch found Ernest Weston at luncheon with another gentlemen at one o'clock the next day. This other gentleman, George Weston, a cousin, was introduced to Hatch. Hatch instantly remembered George Weston as one of the heirs of the original Weston estate.

Hatch and Ernest Weston knew one another. They had met frequently during the ten years that Hatch had been a newspaper reporter. Weston had always been courteous to him, and the reporter was in doubt as to whether to bring up the subject about which he had sought him out. The broker brought it up himself, smilingly.

"Well, what is it this time?" he asked. "I suppose it is the ghost down on the South Shore. Have you heard much about this ghost story?"

"I have seen the ghost!" Hatch answered.

"You have?"

George Weston echoed the words and leaned forward to listen with a new interest in his eyes. Hatch told what had happened in the haunted house—all of it. The two men listened with the keenest attention.

"By George!" exclaimed Ernest Weston, when Hatch had finished. "How do you explain it?"

"I can't," said Hatch, flatly. "I can offer no possible solution. I am not a fool to be tricked by illusion, nor am I one which imagines things, but I can offer no explanation of this."

"It must be a trick of some sort," said George Weston.

"I was positive of that," said Hatch, "but if it is a trick, it is the cleverest I ever saw."

The conversation then turned to the old story of missing jewels and a tragedy in the house fifty years before. Now Hatch was asking the questions suggested by The Thinking Machine; he himself hardly knew why, but he asked them just the same.

"Well, the full story of that affair, the tragedy there, would open up an old chapter in our family which is nothing to be ashamed of, of course," said Ernest Weston, frankly; "still it is something we have not paid much attention to for many years. Perhaps George here knows the story better than I do. His mother, then a bride, was told the story by my grandmother."

Ernest Weston and Hatch looked inquiringly at George Weston.

"Yes, I've heard my mother tell of it," George began, "but it was a long time ago. As I remember it, my great-grandfather, who built the house, was a wealthy man. As fortunes went in those days, he was probably worth a million dollars.

"A part of this fortune—about one hundred thousand dollars—was in jewels, which had come with the family from England. Many of those pieces would be of far greater value now than they were then.

"The problem of keeping these jewels safe was a difficult one. This was before the time of safety deposit vaults. My great-grandfather conceived the idea of hiding the jewels in the old place down on the South Shore, instead of keeping them in the house he had in Boston.

"His plan was to reach the South Shore at night, in order not to attract attention to himself, to hide the jewels in the house, and then leave that same night for Boston. Just what happened at that time no one ever knew."

George Weston paused a moment.

"The next morning my great-grandfather was found on the veranda of the house. His skull had been fractured—and he died without regaining consciousness. In the house a man was found dead. No one knew who he was; no one within a radius of many miles of the place had ever seen him.

"This led to all sorts of guesswork. The one explanation the family has always accepted, was that my great-grandfather had gone to the house in the dark, had met some one who was stopping there that night for shelter from the intense cold, that this man learned of the jewels, that he had tried robbery and there was a fight.

"In this fight the stranger was killed inside the house, and my great-grandfather, injured, had tried to leave the house for aid. He collapsed on the veranda where he was found, and died. That's all we can guess reasonably about the matter."

"Were the jewels ever found?" asked the reporter.

"No. They were not on the dead man, nor were they in the possession of my great-grandfather."

"It is reasonable to suppose then, that there was a third man and that he got away with the jewels?" asked Ernest Weston.

"It seemed so, and for a long time this theory was accepted," answered George. "But the fact remained that only two trails of footsteps led to the house and none of them led out. If none could be found going out it was impossible that anyone came out."

Again there was silence. Ernest Weston sipped his coffee slowly.

"It would seem from that," he said, at last, "that the jewels were hidden before the tragedy, and have never been found."

George Weston smiled.

"Off and on for twenty years the place was searched, according to my mother's story," George said. "Every inch of the cellar was dug up; every possible nook and corner was searched. Finally the entire matter passed out of the minds of those who knew of it, and I doubt if it has ever been referred to again until now."

"A search even now might almost be worthwhile, might it not?" asked Ernest Weston.

George Weston laughed aloud.

"It might be," he said, "but I have some doubt. Something searched for for twenty years would not be easily found."

No one spoke for a moment.

Ernest Weston continued, "This ghost thing, I'm interested in that. Suppose we make up a ghost party and go down tonight. My contractor declares he can't get men to work there."

"I would be glad to go," said George Weston, "but I'm running over to the Vandergrift dance in Providence tonight."

"How about you, Hatch?"

"I'll go, yes," said Hatch. "As one of several," he added with a smile.

"Well, then, suppose we say the constable and you and I?" asked the broker. "Tonight?"

"All right."

After making arrangements to meet the broker later that afternoon, he rushed away to see The Thinking Machine. The scientist listened, then resumed some chemical test he was making.

"Can't you go down with us tonight?" Hatch asked.

"No," said the other. "I'm going to read a paper before a scientific society. That will take me all evening."

"Tomorrow night?" Hatch insisted.

"No—the next night."

Hatch and Ernest Weston took a night train that evening, and on their arrival in the village got hold of the town constable.

"Will you go with us?" was the question.

"Both of you going?" was the counter-question.

"Yes."

"I'll go," said the constable promptly. "Ghost!" He laughed scornfully. "I'll have him in jail by morning."

"No shooting, now," warned Mr. Weston. "There must be somebody back of this somewhere; we understand that, but there is no crime that we know of. The worst is possible trespassing."

"I'll get him all right," responded the constable.

That night, at about ten o'clock, the three men went into the dark, forbidding house. They took their posts on the stairs where Hatch had sat when he saw the THING—whatever it was. There they waited. The constable moved nervously from time to time, but neither of the others paid any attention to him.

At last the—the THING appeared. There had been a preliminary sound as of something running across the floor, then suddenly a flaming figure of white seemed to emerge into being in the reception room. It was exactly as Hatch had described it to The Thinking Machine.

Dazed, the three men looked on, as the figure raised a hand, pointed toward them, and wrote a word in the air—in the very air itself! The finger merely waved, and there floating before them, were letters, flaming letters, in the utter darkness. This time the word was: "Death."

Fighting the fear which was gripping him again, Hatch remembered that The Thinking Machine had asked him if the handwriting was that of a man or woman; now he tried to see. It was as if drawn on a blackboard, and there was a queer twist to the loop at the bottom. He sniffed to see if there was an odor of any sort. There was not.

Suddenly he felt quick, vigorous action from the constable behind him. There was a roar and a flash in his ear. The constable had fired at the THING. Then came the cry and laugh—almost a laugh of derision—that Hatch had heard before! For one instant the figure lingered and then, before their eyes, faded again into utter blackness. Where it had been was nothing—nothing.

The constable's shot had had no effect.

Three deeply mystified men passed down the hill to the village from the old house. Ernest Weston, the owner, had not spoken since before the—the THING appeared there in the reception room, or was it in the library? He was not certain—he couldn't have told. Suddenly he turned to the constable.

"I told you not to shoot."

"I was there in my official capacity," said the constable, "and I shoot when I want to."

"But the shot did no harm," Hatch put in.

"Yet, I would swear it went right through it," said the constable. "I can shoot."

Mr. Weston was arguing with himself. He was a cold-blooded man of business; his mind was not one to play him tricks. Yet he could conceive no explana-

73

tion of what he had seen. Again in his room in the little hotel, where they spent the remainder of the night, he stared blankly at the reporter.

"Can you imagine any way it could be done?"

Hatch shook his head.

"It isn't a spook, of course," Ernest Weston went on, with a nervous smile; "but—but I'm sorry I went. I don't think I shall have the contracting work done there as I thought."

They slept fitfully and took an early train back to Boston. As they were about to separate at the South Station, the broker had a last word to say.

"I'm going to solve this thing," he declared, determinedly. "I know one man at least who isn't afraid of it—or of anything else. I'm going to send him down to keep a lookout and take care of the place. His name is O'Heagan, and he's a fighting Irishman. If he and that —that—THING ever get mixed up together . . ."

Like a schoolboy with a hopeless problem, Hatch went straight to The Thinking Machine with the latest developments. The scientist paused just long enough in his work to hear it.

"Did you notice the handwriting?" he demanded.

"Yes," was the reply; "so far as I *could* notice the style of a handwriting that floated in air."

"Man's or woman's?"

Hatch was puzzled.

"I couldn't judge," he said. "It seemed to be a bold

style, whatever it was. I remember the capital D clearly."

"Was it anything like the handwriting of the broker —what's-his-name—Ernest Weston?"

"I never saw his handwriting."

"Look at some of it, then, particularly the capital D's," instructed The Thinking Machine. Then, after a pause: "You say the figure is white and appears to be in flames?"

"Yes."

"Does it give out any light? That is, does it light up a room, for instance?"

"I don't quite know what you mean."

"When you go into a room with a lamp," explained The Thinking Machine, "it lights the room. Does this thing do that? Can you see the floor or walls or anything by the light of the figure itself?"

"No," replied Hatch, positively.

"I'll go down with you tomorrow night," said the scientist, as if that were all.

"Thanks," replied Hatch, and he went away.

The next day about noon he called at Ernest Weston's office. The broker was in.

"Did you send down your man O'Heagan?" Hatch asked.

"Yes," said the broker. He was almost smiling.

"What happened?"

"He's outside. I'll let him tell you."

The broker went to the door and spoke to someone.

Then O'Heagan entered. He was a big, blue-eyed Irishman, frankly freckled and red-headed—one of those men who look trouble in the face and are glad of it if the trouble can be reduced to a fighting basis.

"Tell Mr. Hatch what happened last night," requested the broker.

O'Heagan told his story. He, too, had sought to get hold of the flaming figure. As he ran for it, it disappeared, was obliterated, wiped out, gone, and he found himself groping in the darkness of the room beyond, the library. Like Hatch, he took the nearest way out, which happened to be through a window already smashed.

"Outside," he went on, "I began to think about it. I saw there was nothing to be afraid of, but you couldn't have convinced me of that when I was inside. I took a lantern in one hand and a revolver in the other and went all over that house. There was nothing; if there had been, we would have had it out right there. But there was *nothing*. So I started out to the barn, where I had put a cot in a room.

"I went upstairs to this room—it was then about two o'clock—and went to sleep. It seemed to be an hour or so later when I awoke suddenly—I knew something was happening. And the Lord forgive me if I'm a liar, but there was a cat—a ghost cat in my room, racing around like mad. I just naturally got up to see what was the matter and rushed for the door. The cat beat me to it, and cut a flaming streak through the night.

"The cat looked just like the thing inside the house —that is, it was a sort of shadowy, waving white light like it might be afire. I went back to bed in disgust, to sleep it off. You see, sir," he apologized to Ernest Weston, "there hadn't been anything yet I could put my hands on."

"Was that all?" asked Hatch, smilingly.

"Just the beginning. Next morning when I awoke I was bound to my cot, hard and fast. My hands were tied and my feet were tied, and all I could do was lie there and yell. After a while, it seemed years, I heard some one outside and shouted louder than ever. Then the constable come up and let me loose. I told him all about it—and then I came to Boston. And with your permission, Mr. Weston, I resign right now. I'm not afraid of anything I can fight, but when I can't get hold of it—well—"

Later, Hatch joined The Thinking Machine. They caught a train for the little village by the sea. On the way The Thinking Machine asked a few questions, but most of the time he was silent, squinting out the window. Hatch respected his silence, and only answered questions.

"Did you see Ernest Weston's handwriting?" was the first of these.

"Yes."

"The capital D's?"

"They are not unlike the one the—the THING wrote, but they are not wholly like it," was the reply.

"Do you know anyone in Providence who can get some information for you?" was the next query.

"Yes."

"Get him by long-distance phone when we get to this place and let me talk to him a moment."

Half an hour later The Thinking Machine was talking over the long-distance phone to the Providence correspondent of Hatch's paper. What he said or what he learned was not revealed to the wondering reporter, but he came out after several minutes, only to re-enter the booth and remain for another half hour.

"Now," he said.

Together they went to the haunted house. At the entrance to the grounds something else occurred to The Thinking Machine.

"Run over to the phone and call Ernest Weston," he directed. "Ask him if he has a motorboat or if his cousin has one. We might need one. Also find out what kind of a boat it is—electric or gasoline."

Hatch returned to the village and left the scientist alone, sitting on the veranda gazing out over the sea. When Hatch returned he was still in the same position.

"Well?" he asked.

"Ernest Weston has no motorboat," the reporter informed him. "George Weston has an electric, but we can't get it because it is being used. Maybe I can get one somewhere else if you particularly want it."

"Never mind," said The Thinking Machine. He spoke as if he had entirely lost interest in the matter.

Together they started around the house to the kitchen door.

"What's the next move?" asked Hatch.

"I'm going to find the jewels," was the startling reply.

"Find them?" Hatch repeated.

"Certainly."

They entered the house through the kitchen and the scientist squinted this way and that, through the reception room, the library, and finally the back hallway. Here a closed door in the floor led to a cellar.

In the cellar they found heaps of litter. It was damp and chilly and dark. The Thinking Machine stood in the center, or as near the center as he could stand, because the base of the chimney occupied this precise spot, and apparently did some mental calculation.

From that point he started around the walls, solidly built of stone, stooping and running his fingers along the stones as he walked. He made the entire circuit as Hatch looked on. Then he made it again, but this time with his hands raised above his head, feeling the walls carefully as he went. He repeated this at the chimney, going carefully around the masonry, high and low.

"Dear me, dear me!" he exclaimed. "You are taller than I am, Mr. Hatch. Please feel carefully around the top of this chimney base and see if the rocks are all solidly set."

Hatch then began a tour. At last one of the great

stones which formed this base trembled under his hand.

"It's loose," he said.

"Take it out."

It came out after a deal of tugging.

"Put your hand in there and pull out what you find," was the next order. Hatch obeyed. He found a wooden box, about eight inches square, and handed it to The Thinking Macine.

A quick wrench caused the decaying wood to crumble. Tumbling out of the box were the jewels which had been lost for fifty years.

Excitement, long restrained, burst from Hatch in a laugh—almost hysterical. He stooped and gathered up the fallen jewelry and handed it to The Thinking Machine, who stared at him in mild surprise.

"What's the matter?" inquired the scientist.

"Nothing," Hatch assured him, but again he laughed. The heavy stone which had been pulled out of place was lifted up and forced back into position, and together they returned to the village, with the long-lost jewelry in their pockets.

"How did you do it?" asked Hatch. He shook his head. "How did you ever do it?"

"Two and two always make four," was the reply. "It was merely a sum in addition." There was a pause as they walked on, then: "Don't say anything about finding this. Don't even hint at it in any way, until you have my permission to do so."

Hatch had no intention of doing so. In his mind's eye he saw a story, a great, vivid, startling story spread all over his newspaper about flaming phantoms and treasure trove—$100,000 in jewels. It staggered him. Of course, he would say nothing about it— or even hint at it, yet. But when he did say something about it . . . !

As they walked back to the village, the professor said: "Mr. Hatch, will you wire to Mr. Weston—Ernest Weston—and ask him to be sure to come tonight. Impress on him the fact that it is a matter of the greatest importance."

Instead of telegraphing, Hatch went to the telephone and spoke to Weston at his club. The trip would interfere with some other plans, the broker explained, but he would come. The Thinking Machine, meanwhile, had been conversing with the constable and had given some sort of instructions which evidently amazed that official exceedingly.

"And not one word or hint of it to anyone," said The Thinking Machine. "Least of all to the members of your family."

The Thinking Machine and Hatch had their supper thoughtfully that evening in the little village "hotel." Only once did Hatch break the silence.

"You told me to see Ernest Weston's handwriting," he said. "Of course, you knew he was with the con-

stable and myself when we saw the THING, therefore
it would have been impossible . . ."

"Nothing is impossible," broke in The Thinking Machine. "Don't say that, please."

"I mean that, as he was with us—"

"We'll end the ghost story tonight," interrupted the
scientist.

Ernest Weston arrived on the nine-thirty train and
had a long, earnest conversation with The Thinking
Machine, while Hatch was permitted to cool his toes in
solitude. At last they joined the reporter.

"Take a revolver by all means," instructed The
Thinking Machine.

"Do you think that necessary?" asked Weston.

"It is—absolutely," was the emphatic response.

Mr. Weston left them after awhile, but no information was forthcoming. In a general sort of way Hatch
knew that The Thinking Machine was to go to the
haunted house, but he didn't know when; he didn't
even know if he was to accompany him.

At last they started, The Thinking Machine swinging
a hammer he had borrowed from his landlord. The
night was an inky black. The very road at their feet
was invisible. They stumbled frequently as they
walked on up the cliff toward the house, which stood
out against the sky. They entered by way of the
kitchen, and passed through to the stairs in the main
hall. There Hatch indicated in the darkness the spot
from which he had twice seen the flaming phantom.

"You go to the drawing room behind here," The Thinking Machine instructed. "Don't make any noise whatever."

For hours they waited, neither seeing the other. Hatch heard his heart thumping heavily; if only he could see the Professor! With an effort he controlled his rapidly growing nervousness and waited, impatiently. The Thinking Machine sat perfectly rigid on the stair, the hammer in his right hand, squinting steadily through the darkness.

At last there was a noise, a very slight sound. It was as if something had glided across the floor. Then a misty light appeared in the reception hall, or was it in the library?

Gradually the light grew and spread, a misty whiteness which was unmistakably light, but which did not illuminate anything around it. The Thinking Machine saw it without the tremor of a nerve; saw the mistiness grow more distinct in certain places, saw these lines gradually emerge into the figure of a person, a person who was the center of a white light.

Then the mistiness fell away and The Thinking Machine saw the outline in bold relief. It was that of a tall figure, clothed in a robe, with head covered by a sort of hood, also luminous. As The Thinking Machine looked, he saw an arm raised, and in the hand he saw a dagger. And yet The Thinking Machine had not begun to be nervous; he was only interested.

As he looked, the other hand of the apparition was

raised and seemed to point directly at him. It moved
through the air in bold sweeps, and The Thinking Machine saw the word *"Death,"* written luminously, in air
swimming before his eyes. There came a wild, demoni-
acal shriek of laughter from somewhere. Slowly, slowly
the scientist crept down the steps in his stocking feet,
silent as the apparition itself, with the hammer still in
his hand. He crept on . . . toward the figure. Hatch,
not knowing the movements of The Thinking Machine,
stood waiting for something, he didn't know what.
Then the thing he had been waiting for happened.
There was a sudden loud clatter as of broken glass, the
phantom and the writing faded, crumbled up, disappeared, and somewhere in the old house there was the
hurried sound of steps. At last the reporter heard his
name called quietly. It was The Thinking Machine.

"Mr. Hatch, come here."

The reporter started, blundering through the darkness toward the point from which the voice had come.
Some irresistible thing swept down upon him; a crash-
ing blow descended on his head, vivid lights flashed
before his eyes; he fell. After awhile, from a great distance, it seemed, he heard faintly a pistol shot.

When Hatch fully recovered consciousness it was
with the light of a match flickering before his eyes.
The match was in the hand of The Thinking Machine,
who squinted anxiously at him as he grasped his left
wrist. Hatch, instantly himself again, sat up suddenly.

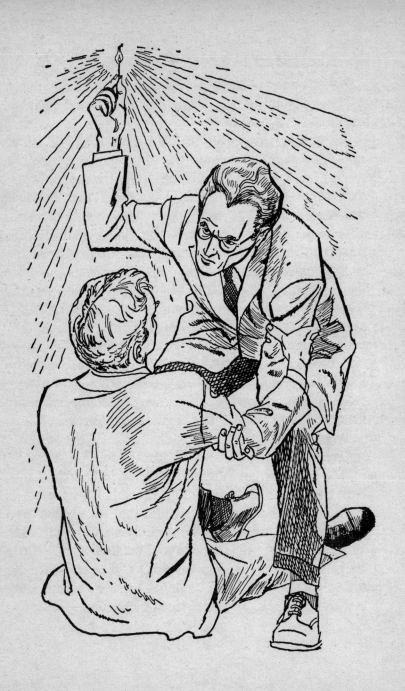

"What's the matter?" he demanded.

"How's your head?" came the Professor's question, in turn.

"Oh!" Hatch suddenly recalled those incidents which had immediately preceded the crash on his head. "Oh, it's all right, my head, I mean. What happened?"

"Get up and come along," requested The Thinking Machine, tartly. "A man's been shot down here."

Hatch arose and followed the slight figure of the scientist through the front door, and toward the water. A light glimmered near the water and was dimly reflected; above, the clouds had cleared somewhat and the moon was struggling through.

"What hit me, anyhow?" Hatch demanded, as they walked along. He rubbed his head ruefully.

"The ghost," said the scientist. "I think probably he has a bullet in him now . . . the ghost."

Then the figure of the town constable emerged from the darkness of the night and approached.

"Who's that?"

"Professor Van Dusen and Mr. Hatch."

"Mr. Weston got him all right," said the constable, and there was satisfaction in his tone. "He tried to come out the back way, but I had that fastened, as you told me; and he came through the front way. Mr. Weston tried to stop him, and he raised the knife to strike him; then Mr. Weston fired a shot. It broke his arm, I think. Mr. Weston is down there with him now."

The Thinking Machine turned to the reporter.

"Wait here for me, with the constable," he directed. "If the man is hurt he needs attention. I happen to be a doctor; I can help him. Don't come unless I call."

For a long while the constable and the reporter waited. The constable talked away, but Hatch listened impatiently. He was eager to find out what was happening. What were The Thinking Machine and Weston doing? Where was the phantom?

After half an hour the light disappeared, and Hatch heard the swift, quick churning of water, and a sound as of a powerful motorboat being maneuvered.

"All right down there?" Hatch called.

"All right," came the response.

Again there was silence. Then Ernest Weston and The Thinking Machine came up.

"Where is the other man?" asked Hatch.

"The ghost—where is he?" echoed the constable.

"He escaped in the motorboat," replied Ernest Weston.

"Escaped?" exclaimed Hatch and the constable together.

"Yes, escaped," repeated The Thinking Machine, irritably. "Mr. Hatch, let's go to the hotel."

Struggling with a sense of keen disappointment, Hatch followed the other two men silently. The constable walked beside him, also silent. At last they reached the hotel and bade the constable, a sadly puzzled, bewildered and crestfallen man, goodnight.

Upstairs the three men sat, Hatch impatiently wait-ing for an explanation. Mr. Weston lounged back on an easy chair. The Thinking Machine sat with finger tips pressed together, studying the ceiling.

"Mr. Weston, you understand, of course, that I came into this thing to aid Mr. Hatch?" he asked.

"Certainly," was the response. "I will only ask a favor of him when you conclude."

The Thinking Machine changed his position slightly, readjusted his thick glasses for a long, comfortable squint, and told the story, from the beginning, as he always did.

"Mr. Hatch came to me in a state of abject fear and told me of the mystery. It would be needless to go over his examination of the house. It is enough to say that he noted and told me of four large mirrors in the dining room and living room of the house; that he heard and brought to me the stories in detail of a tragedy in the old house and missing jewels, valued at a hundred thousand dollars, or more.

"He told me of his trip to the house that night, and of actually seeing the phantom. I have found in the past that Mr. Hatch is a cool, level-headed young man not given to imagining things which do not exist. Therefore, I knew that any act of charlatanism must be clever, exceedingly clever, to bring about such a state of mind in him.

"Mr. Hatch saw, as others had seen, the figure of a phantom in the reception room near the door of the library, or in the library near the door of the reception room. He couldn't tell exactly where but he knew it was near the door. Preceding the appearance of the figure, he heard a slight noise which he attributed to a rat running across the floor. Yet the house had not been occupied for five years. Rodents rarely remain in a house—I may say never—for that long if it is uninhabited. Therefore, what was this noise? A noise made by the apparition itself? How?

"Now, there is only one white light of the kind Mr. Hatch described known to science. It seems almost superfluous to name it. It is phosphorus, compounded with Fuller's earth and glycerine and one or two other chemicals, so it will not instantly flame as it does in its pure state when exposed to air. Phosphorus has a very pronounced odor if one is within, say, twenty feet of it. Did Mr. Hatch smell anything? No.

"Now, here we have several facts, these being that the apparition in appearing made a slight noise; that phosphorus was the luminous quality; that Mr. Hatch did not smell phosphorus even when he ran to the spot where the phantom had appeared. Two and two make four; Mr. Hatch saw phosphorus, passed through the spot where he had seen it, but did not smell it, therefore it was not there. It was a reflection he saw —a reflection of phosphorus. So far, so good.

"Mr. Hatch saw a finger lifted and write a luminous word in the air. Again he did not actually see this; he saw a reflection of it. This first impression of mine was substantiated by the fact that when he rushed for the phantom *a part of it* disappeared, first half of it, he said—then the other half. So his extended hands grasped only air.

"Obviously those reflections had been made on something, probably a mirror as the most perfect ordinary reflecting surface. Yet he actually passed through the spot where he had seen the apparition and had not struck a mirror. He found himself in another room, the library, having gone through a door which, that afternoon, he had himself closed. He did not open it then.

"Instantly a sliding mirror suggested itself to me to fit all these conditions. He saw the apparition in the door, then saw only half of it, then all of it disappeared. He passed through the spot where it had been. All of this would have happened easily if a large mirror, working as a sliding door, and hidden in the wall, were there. Is it clear?"

"Perfectly," said Ernest Weston.

"Yes," said Hatch, eagerly. "Go on."

"This sliding mirror, too, might have made the noise which Mr. Hatch imagined was a rat. Mr. Hatch had previously told me of four large mirrors in the living and dining rooms. With these, from the position in which he said they were, I readily saw how the reflection could have been made.

"In a general sort of way, in my own mind, I had accounted for the phantom. Why was it there? This seemed a more difficult problem. It was possible that it had been put there for amusement, but I did not wholly accept this. Why? Partly because no one had ever heard of it until the workmen went there. Why did it appear just at the moment they went to begin the work Mr. Weston had ordered? Was the purpose to keep the workmen away?

"These questions arose in my mind in order. Then, as Mr. Hatch had told me of a tragedy in the house and hidden jewels, I asked him about it in order to find out more. I called his attention to the fact that it would be a queer circumstance if these jewels were still somewhere in the old house. Suppose some one who knew of their existence were searching for them, believed he could find them, and wanted something which would effectively drive away any inquiring persons, tramps, or villagers, who might appear there at night. A ghost? Perhaps.

"Suppose some one wanted to give the old house such a reputation that Mr. Weston would not care to undertake the work of repair and refurnishing. A ghost? Again perhaps. In a shallow mind this ghost might have been interpreted even as an effort to prevent the marriage of Miss Everard and Mr. Weston. Therefore Mr. Hatch was instructed to get all the facts possible about you, Mr. Weston, and members of your family. I reasoned that members of your own family would be more likely to know of the lost jewels than anyone else after a lapse of fifty years.

"Well, what Mr. Hatch learned from you and your cousin, George Weston, instantly, in my mind, established a motive for the ghost. It was, as I had supposed possible, an effort to drive workmen away, perhaps only for a time, while a search was made for the jewels. The old tragedy in the house was a good pretext to hang a ghost on. A clever mind conceived it and a clever mind put it into operation.

"Now, what one person knew most about the jewels? Your cousin George, Mr. Weston. Had he recently acquired any new information as to these jewels? I didn't know. I thought it possible. Why? On his own statement that his mother, then a bride, got the story of the entire affair direct from his great-grandmother, who remembered more of it than anybody else—who might even have heard his great-grandfather say where he intended hiding the jewels."

The Thinking Machine paused for a little while, shifted his position, then went on:

"George Weston refused to go with you, Mr. Weston, and Mr. Hatch, to the ghost party, as you called it, because he said he was going to a ball in Providence that night. He did not go to Providence; I learned that from your correspondent there, Mr. Hatch; so George Weston might, possibly, have gone to the ghost party after all.

"After I looked over the situation down there it occurred to me that the most feasible way for a person, who wished to avoid being seen in the village, as the perpetrator of the ghost did, was to go to and from the place at night in a motorboat. He could easily run in the dark and land at the foot of the cliff, and no soul in the village would be any the wiser. Did George Weston have a motorboat? Yes, an electric, which runs almost silently.

"From this point the entire matter was comparatively simple. I *knew*—the pure logic of it told me—how the ghost was made to appear and disappear; one look at the house inside convinced me beyond all doubt. I knew the motive for the ghost—a search for the jewels. I knew, or thought I knew, the name of the man who was seeking the jewels; the man who had fullest knowledge and fullest opportunity, the man whose brain was clever enough to devise the scheme. Then, the next step was to prove what I knew. The first thing was to find the jewels."

"Find the jewels?" Weston repeated, with a slight smile.

"Here they are," said The Thinking Machine, quietly.

And there, before the astonished eyes of the broker, he drew out the gems which had been lost for fifty years. Mr. Weston was not merely amazed; he was paralyzed with astonishment. Finally he recovered his voice.

"How did you do it?" he demanded. "Where were they?"

"I used my brain, that's all," was the reply. "I went into the old house seeking them where the owner, under all conditions, would have been most likely to hide them, and there I found them."

"But—but—" stammered the broker.

"The man who hid these jewels hid them only temporarily, or at least, that was his purpose," said The Thinking Machine, irritably. "Naturally he would not hide them in the woodwork of the house, because they might burn; he did not bury them in the cellar, because that has been carefully searched. Now, in that house there is nothing except woodwork and chimneys above the cellar. Yet he hid them in the house, proven by the fact that the man he killed was killed in the house, and that the outside ground, covered with snow, showed two sets of tracks into the house and none out. Therefore, he did hide them in the cellar. Where? In the stonework, of course. There was no other place.

"Naturally he would not hide them on a level with the eye, because the spot where he took out and replaced a stone would be apparent if a close search were made. He would, therefore, place them either above or below the eye level. He placed them above. A large loose stone was taken out of the chimney and there was the box with these things."

Mr. Weston stared at The Thinking Machine with a new wonder and admiration in his eyes.

"With the jewels found and disposed of, there remained only to prove the ghost theory by an actual test. I sent for you, Mr. Weston, because I thought possibly, as no actual crime had been committed, it would be better to leave the guilty man to you. When you came I went into the haunted house with a hammer—an ordinary hammer—and waited on the steps.

"At last the ghost appeared. I crept down the steps where I was sitting in my stocking feet. When I reached the luminous phantom I disposed of it for all time by smashing it with a hammer. It shattered a large mirror which ran in the door inside the frame, as I had thought. The crash startled the man who operated the ghost from the top of a box, giving it the appearance of extreme height. He started out through the kitchen, as he had entered. The constable had barred that door after the man entered; therefore, the ghost turned and came toward the front door of the house. There he ran into and struck down Mr. Hatch, and ran out through the front door, which I afterwards found was not securely fastened. You know the rest; how you found the motorboat and waited there for him; how he came there, and—"

"Tried to stab me," Ernest Weston supplied. "I had to shoot to save myself."

"Well, the wound is slight," said The Thinking Machine. "His arm will heal up in a little while. I think, perhaps, a little trip of four or five years in Europe, at your expense, in return for the jewels, might restore him to health."

"I was thinking of that myself," said the broker, quietly. "Of course, I couldn't prosecute."

"The ghost, then, was—?" Hatch began.

"George Weston, my cousin," said the broker. "There are some things in this story which I hope you may see fit to leave unsaid, if you can do so with justice to yourself."

Hatch considered it.

"I think there are," he said finally, and he turned to The Thinking Machine. "Just where was the man who operated the phantom?"

"In the dining room, beside the butler's pantry," was the reply. "With that pantry door closed, he put on the robe already covered with phosphorus, and merely stepped out. The figure was reflected in the tall mirror directly in front, as you enter the dining room from the back; from there reflected to the mirror on the opposite wall in the living room; and thence reflected to the sliding mirror in the door which led from the reception hall to the library. This is the one I smashed."

"And how was the writing done?"

"Oh, that? Of course that was done by reversed writing on a piece of clear glass held before the apparition as he posed. This made it appear normal to anyone who might see the last reflection in the reception hall."

All sat silent for a time. At length Ernest Weston arose, thanked the scientist for the recovery of the jewels, bade them all good-night and was about to go out. Mechanically Hatch was following. At the door he turned back for the last question.

"How was it that the shot the constable fired didn't break the mirror?"

"Because he was nervous and the bullet struck the door beside the mirror," was the reply. "I dug it out with a knife. Good-night."

The Mystery

of the

Silver Box

"REALLY clever criminals are never found out, for the simple reason that their crimes are never discovered," remarked Professor Augustus S. F. X. Van Dusen to his visitor.

Professor Van Dusen was more widely known as The Thinking Machine—the amazing scientist who could find the answer to any problem devised by man. His brilliant mind set in order and analyzed each fact in a mystery with the efficiency of a smooth-running engine. Then, as night follows day, The Thinking Machine could be depended upon to announce the solution. He preferred, of course, baffling crimes in which he could pit his nimble mind against that of the most conniving and cunning foe.

"You see," continued the scientist, "the expert criminal regards as perfect only a crime which does not and cannot be made to appear a crime at all; one that can never involve him."

The Thinking Machine was speaking to J. Morgan Grayson, the well-known millionaire businessman. Mr. Grayson opened his mouth to speak, but the scientist continued:

"Yes, Mr. Grayson, there are a few very clever people actively engaged in crime. We never hear of them because they are never caught. We never even suspect them because they make no mistake. But their crimes can be solved if all the facts are properly studied. Every scientist knows that we gain knowledge through observation and clear thinking. And clear thinking—or logic—tells us that two and two make four, not sometimes, but all the time. Solving a mystery is as simple as that."

Mr. Grayson took a step forward and looked into the drawn, lean face of the scientist. The enormous straw-yellow head was cushioned against a leather chair, the squinting watery blue eyes turned upward, the slender white fingers at rest, tip to tip. The businessman drew a long breath, as if sighing over his troubles.

"I have been informed that you are a remarkable man," he said at last slowly. "I believe that. Quinton

Frazer, my banker, told me how you once managed to escape from a prison death cell within a week's time—"

"That was really nothing," interrupted The Thinking Machine. "I was challenged to prove that a man could *think* his way out of a prison and proceeded to do just that."

"I've come to you for help in something which I think is more challenging than the famous problem of Cell 13," said Mr. Grayson.

The Thinking Machine turned to the worried businessman. "State your problem."

"It isn't a crime—that is, a crime that can be reached by law," Mr. Grayson hurried on, "but it has cost me millions, perhaps as much as ten million dollars! Briefly, there is an information leak at my office. My business plans become known to others almost at the time I have perfected them. My plans are large; I have millions of dollars at stake; and the need for secrecy is great. For years I have been able to preserve this secrecy; but half a dozen times in the last eight weeks my plans have become known to my competitors. You can't imagine what a tremendous burden it is in business to have someone know your next move to the smallest detail and, by knowing, win your customers away."

"No, I don't know your world of business, Mr. Grayson," remarked The Thinking Machine. "Give me an instance."

"Well, take this last case," came the answer. "I am a manufacturer of machines and tools that are used in factories. Recently I decided to get more business by sending salesmen to new industrial areas out West. My salesmen were to demonstrate my equipment.

"At first my plan was a great successs. Salesmen sold whatever they were demonstrating—right at the factory—and also were given extra orders. That's how much the factory owners appreciated this on-the-spot service.

"Suddenly my plan backfired. My men reported that wherever they went, they were too late. My biggest business rival had already sent *his* salesmen out to demonstrate *his* products *at a lower price*—to *my* customers. I had made detailed studies to see which factories were in need of special equipment, hoping to show my customers how they could save money. Yet the day before my salesmen arrived, my rival's men were on hand with his equipment—to snatch away my sales!"

The Thinking Machine walked to a window. "So now you want to know how—and where—information is leaking from your office."

"Precisely."

"Well, to whom do you tell your business plans?"

"No one, except my personal secretary."

"Who is he, please?"

"I have a woman secretary—Miss Evelyn Winthrop. She has been with me for six years—more than five years before this information leak began. I have always trusted her."

"No one else knows your business?"

"No," replied Mr. Grayson. "I learned many years ago that no one could keep my secrets as well as I do —there are too many temptations. So, I never mention my plans to anyone—never—to anyone!"

"Except your secretary," corrected the scientist.

"I work for days, weeks, sometimes months, perfecting plans, and it's all in my head, not on paper—not a scratch of it," explained Mr. Grayson. "When I say that I tell Miss Winthrop of my plans, I mean that she knows them only a few minutes or so before I give orders to carry them out. For instance, this week, I planned to send salesmen to Oklahoma with new oil drills. My district managers didn't know of this plan. Miss Winthrop never heard of it until the morning I decided to send out salesmen. Then I dictated to her, as I always do, some short letters of instructions to my district managers. That is all Miss Winthrop knew of my Oklahoma plan."

"You outlined the plan in those letters?"

"No. They merely told my managers which salesmen I wanted for Oklahoma and the cost of various drilling machinery."

"But a shrewd person, knowing the contents of all those letters, could have learned what you intended to do?" The Thinking Machine asked.

"Yes; but no one person knew the contents of *all*

the letters. No one manager knew what was in the *other* letters. Miss Winthrop and I were the only two human beings who knew all that was in them."

The Thinking Machine sat silent for so long that Mr. Grayson began to fidget in his chair. "Who was in your office besides you and Miss Winthrop before the letters were sent?" he asked at last.

"No one. On the morning that I dictated those letters, no one entered my office. In fact, neither of us left the office that day. We had lunch sent up. Yet before the day ended, I received two phone calls from friends in Oklahoma who are in the oil business.

They had received telegrams from my rival offering drills at unusually low prices. They were calling to see if I could meet these prices. If not, they said, they felt that they'd have to buy the drills from him."

"Did Miss Winthrop go out after she finished typing the letters?" asked The Thinking Machine.

"No, she didn't even leave her desk."

"Perhaps she sent something out—carbon copies of the letters?"

"No."

"Or called up a friend on the telephone?" continued The Thinking Machine quietly.

"Nor that," said Mr. Grayson.

"Or signaled to someone through the window?"

"No, she finished the letters, then remained quietly at her desk, working hard for the rest of the day. She hardly moved away from it."

The Thinking Machine stared into Mr. Grayson's eyes. "Could someone have listened at the door or window while you were dictating?"

"No, my office is sixteen stories up, fronting the street, and there is no fire escape."

"And the door?"

"If you know the arrangement of my offices, you would see how utterly impossible that would be, because . . ."

"Nothing is impossible, Mr. Grayson," snapped the scientist abruptly. "It might be improbable, but not impossible." He was silent for a moment. "Did either you or your secretary answer a call on the phone?"

"No one called; we called no one."

"Are there any holes or cracks in your flooring or walls or ceilings?" demanded the scientist.

"Private detectives whom I had employed looked for such an opening, and there was none," replied Mr. Grayson.

The Thinking Machine was silent for a long time. Mr. Grayson settled back in his chair patiently.

"Could the letters you wrote have been taken by someone before they were mailed?" asked The Thinking Machine.

"No," exclaimed Mr. Grayson. "I brought this particular batch to the post office myself."

"Very strange! Very strange indeed!" The Thinking Machine rose and paced the length of the room.

"You don't give me credit for the extraordinary care I took, particularly in my plans for Oklahoma," Mr. Grayson continued. "I left positively nothing undone to insure absolute secrecy. And Miss Winthrop, I know, is innocent of any connection with the affair. My private detectives suspected her at first, as you do, and she was watched in and out of my office for weeks. When she was not under my eyes, she was under the eyes of men to whom I had promised a huge reward if they found out how information leaked from my office. She didn't know it then, and doesn't know it now. I am heartily ashamed of it all, because the investigation proved her absolute loyalty to me. On this last day she was directly under my eyes for eight hours; and she didn't make one movement that I didn't note, because the plan meant millions to me. That proved beyond all question that it was no fault of hers. What can I do?"

The Thinking Machine didn't answer. He paused at a window, and for a minute stood motionless there, with eyes narrowed to mere slits.

"I was on the point of discharging Miss Winthrop," Mr. Grayson went on, "but her innocence was so thoroughly proved to me by this last affair that it would have been unjust, and so—"

Suddenly the scientist turned upon his visitor. "Do you talk in your sleep?" he asked.

"No," was the prompt reply. "I had thought of that, too. It is beyond all ordinary things, Professor. Yet there is a leak that is costing me millions."

"It comes down to this, Mr. Grayson," The Thinking Machine informed him. "If only you and Miss Winthrop knew those plans, and no one else, and they did leak, and were not deduced from other things, then either you or she permitted them to leak, intentionally or unintentionally. That is as pure logic as two and two make four; there is no need to argue it."

"Well, of course, I didn't," said Mr. Grayson.

"Then Miss Winthrop did," declared The Thinking Machine finally, positively; "unless your business rival is a great mind reader! By the way, what is his name?"

106

"Ralph Matthews," said Mr. Grayson.

The Thinking Machine went to a desk, addressed an envelope, folded a sheet of paper, placed it inside, then sealed it. At length he turned back to his visitor. "Is Miss Winthrop at your office now?"

"Yes."

"Let us go there, then."

A few minutes later Mr. Grayson ushered The Thinking Machine into his private office. The only person there was a young woman working at her desk near a window. Mr. Grayson asked The Thinking Machine to have a seat. Instead of sitting, however, the scientist went straight to Miss Winthrop and handed her a sealed envelope.

"Mr. Ralph Matthews asked me to hand you this," he said.

The young woman glanced up into his face frankly, yet with a certain shyness, took the envelope, and turned it curiously in her hand.

"Ralph Matthews," she repeated, as if the name was a strange one. "I don't think I know him."

The Thinking Machine stood staring at her almost angrily, as she opened the envelope and drew out the sheet of paper. There was no expression save surprise—bewilderment, rather—to be seen on her face.

"Why, it's a blank sheet!" she remarked puzzled.

The scientist turned suddenly toward Mr. Grayson, who had witnessed the incident with frank astonishment in his eyes. "May I use a telephone, please?" asked The Thinking Machine.

"Certainly," replied Mr. Grayson. "There's one on Miss Winthrop's desk."

The scientist leaned forward over the desk where Miss Winthrop sat, still gazing at him in a sort of bewilderment. He picked up the receiver, and held it to his ear. A few moments later he was talking to his good friend Hutchinson Hatch, a newspaper reporter.

"I'd like you to meet me at my apartment in an hour," said the scientist. "It is very important—and I may have a good story for you."

That was all. He hung up the receiver, paused for a moment to admire an exquisite silver box—a "vanity" box—on Miss Winthrop's desk. It was right next to the telephone. Then he took a seat beside Mr. Grayson and began to talk pleasantly about the weather and cloud formations. Mr. Grayson and Miss Winthrop both had worried expressions—as if expecting sudden trouble.

Professor Augustus S. F. X. Van Dusen—The Thinking Machine—and Hutchinson Hatch, newspaper reporter, were poking around on the roof of an office building. It was a little after midnight. Darkness hung like a veil, with bright star-points breaking through here and there.

For nearly an hour both men had been working in the building that housed the offices of J. Morgan

Grayson. Without Mr. Grayson's knowledge, The
Thinking Machine had arranged to enter the building
and carry out a plan. Its success depended on splicing
a wire to Miss Winthrop's telephone, then running
the wire to the roof. The end of the wire was to be
hooked up to a telephone. This was the task that
Hatch—puzzled as he had never been before—was now
completing.

"Are you sure you know what you are doing?"
asked the reporter.

"I am always sure," snapped The Thinking Machine.

After the wire was connected to the telephone, The
Thinking Machine hid it in a corner of the roof.

"At ten o'clock this morning," he said, "I'd like you back at this phone. Please bring with you the best telegraph operator at your newspaper—one who can follow the fastest tapping of Morse code. We'll have him listen in on this phone from ten o'clock on."

"A telegraph operator?"

"That's what I said—telegraph operator," answered The Thinking Machine. "At ten sharp."

Hatch smiled. He well knew the strange ways of this brilliant scientist, whose mind so accurately illuminated every problem to which it was directed. "We'll be back here at ten—sharp," he said.

At exactly nine that morning, The Thinking Machine called Mr. Grayson, at work in his private office.

"Please answer this question," said the scientist. "Do you know how long Miss Winthrop has owned the little silver box which is now on her desk—near her telephone?"

Mr. Grayson glanced toward his secretary. "Yes," he answered. "I gave it to her last Christmas. I had given her a gold box but she asked to exchange it at my jeweler for one more to her liking—a silver box."

"Ah," exclaimed The Thinking Machine, "that simplifies matters. Now here is what I should like you to do. At 9:45 ask Miss Winthrop to take some dictation. You must give orders for a new business plan of some sort. And you must dictate these orders in a letter precisely as you have in the past. Then have

110

Miss Winthrop type the letter immediately. I shall see you in your office soon after."

"You mean that this business plan must be purely imaginative?" asked Mr. Grayson.

"Yes, but be sure that all details of your plan are absolutely convincing to Miss Winthrop."

At five minutes to ten, Hutchinson Hatch climbed to the roof of Mr. Grayson's office building with Martin Dennison, a telegraph operator.

"Now what's up, Hatch?" asked Dennison, more confused than irritated to find himself on a rooftop at midmorning. "Just what am I doing here, anyway?"

"I'll answer that question," said a high-pitched voice. The Thinking Machine stepped out from behind a skylight on the roof. He handed Dennison a blank sheet of paper and several pencils. Then he walked to the corner of the roof and pointed to the telephone which Hatch had connected earlier in the morning. "Please make yourself as comfortable as possible at this phone, Mr—"

"Martin Dennison, the *Daily American's* top telegrapher," said Hatch. "Mr. Dennison, this is Professor Van Dusen."

"How do you do," said the telegrapher, "all I'd like to know is—"

"What are you doing here," laughed The Thinking Machine. "You are here, Mr. Dennison, to help solve the mystery of the silver box. And quite a clever mystery it is—I should say—it was."

The Thinking Machine handed the phone to Dennison and told him to listen carefully. For several minutes the telegrapher, hearing nothing, had a blank look on his face. Then it suddenly became alert. Nimbly his fingers wrote out words and figures on the sheet of paper.

Hutchinson Hatch still had no idea of what was happening but looked on, tremendously interested. The Thinking Machine waited until Dennison stopped writing. "Let's go down to Mr. Grayson," he said. "The mystery is solved."

Less than five minutes later the door of the private office opened. In walked The Thinking Machine. Silently, he tossed a folded sheet of paper on the desk before Mr. Grayson, and went straight to Miss Winthrop.

"So you did know Ralph Matthews after all?" he asked.

The girl rose from her desk, trembling. "What do you mean, sir?" she demanded.

"You might as well remove the silver box," The Thinking Machine went on. "There is no further need of a phone connection."

Miss Winthrop glanced down at the telephone on her desk. Her hand darted toward it. The silver "vanity" box was directly under the receiver, supporting it, so that all weight was removed from the hook—and the line was open. She snatched the box and the

receiver dropped back on the hook. The Thinking
Machine turned to Mr. Grayson.

"Miss Winthrop," he said, "is responsible for the
flow of information out of your office."

"Miss Winthrop! I can't believe it!"

"Read the paper I gave you," directed The Thinking
Machine coldly. "Perhaps it will enlighten you."

Mr. Grayson opened the sheet, which had remained
folded in his hand, and glanced at what was written
there. Word for word was the entire imaginary business plan which he had dictated to Miss Winthrop
only minutes before. Not one detail of the plan was
left out!

The businessman was astounded. "Miss Winthrop,"
he said at last. "Here is the plan that I dictated. In
some way you made it known to an outsider for whom
it was not intended. I don't know how you did it, of
course; but I understand that you did do it, so—" He
stepped to the door and opened it with grave courtesy.
"You may leave now—for good."

Miss Winthrop made no plea—merely bowed and
went out. Mr. Grayson then turned to The Thinking
Machine and motioned him to a chair. "How did
she do it?" he asked.

"Miss Winthrop is a tremendously clever woman,"
replied The Thinking Machine. "She never told you
that besides being a stenographer-typist she is also a
telegraph operator. She is so expert in each of her
jobs that she combined the two. In other words, in

writing on the typewriter, she was clever enough to be able to *tap her keys in a pattern that is exactly like the Morse telegraphic code*. Any other telegraph operator at the other end of the phone could translate the clicks of the keys into words."

Mr. Grayson was not entirely convinced. "I still don't understand," he said finally.

The Thinking Machine rose and went to Miss Winthrop's desk. "Here is her telephone with the receiver on the hook. It happens that the little silver vanity box, always on Miss Winthrop's desk, is just tall enough to lift this receiver clear off the hook. The moment the receiver is off the hook the line is open.

"Now when she put the box under the phone, a signal flashed on the company switchboard at the receptionist's desk in your outside office. This automatic signal goes on immediately on all switchboards after a phone is lifted from the receiver.

"Your operator, seeing the signal flash, knew that Miss Winthrop's line was open and that she was about to 'telegraph' a message. The operator quickly put through an outside call—probably to a phone in the office of your business rival, Ralph Matthews. A telegraph operator, hired by Mr. Matthews to answer that phone, heard Miss Winthrop typing in code. He could easily report her message, just as my telegrapher has done."

"In other words," said Mr. Grayson, "when I was at my desk and she was at hers, I couldn't see her telephone. It was a simple matter for her to lift the receiver, place the silver box underneath—and hold the line open permanently. The sound of the type-writer—the striking of the keys—would go over the open wire to whomever was listening at the other end."

"Exactly," said The Thinking Machine. "And that is why Miss Winthrop exchanged the gold box at your jeweler. Not because she preferred silver to gold—as she told you—but because the gold vanity box was a little too small. It did not lift the receiver off the hook."

Mr. Grayson stepped outside the office to inform the switchboard operator that her services, too, no longer would be required.

"I think she is gone for good," said The Thinking Machine. "No doubt, she left with Miss Winthrop. I'm afraid, however, that there's nothing you can do to either of them. They were spies for Ralph Matthews and did not break any law. They were too clever for that—but not clever enough to conceal their secret."